ADVANCED MODULAR MATHEMATICS

Statistics 1

for A and AS level

The University of London modular mathematics syllabus

Gerald Westover

for

Published by Collins Educational
An imprint of HarperCollins*Publishers*
77–85 Fulham Palace Road
Hammersmith
London W6 8JB

Reprinted 1995

First published 1995
ISBN 0 00 322397 3

This book was written by Gerald Westover for the National Extension College Trust Ltd. Part of the material was originally written by Mik Wisnieski and Graham Smithers, and additional material was written by Clifford Taylor.

Designed by Derek Lee
Cover design and implementation by Derek Lee
Page layout by Mary Bishop
Project editor, Hugh Hillyard-Parker

The author and publishers thank Pat Perkins and Peter Naylor for their comments on this book.

Printed and bound in the UK by Scotprint Ltd, Musselburgh

National Extension College Trust Ltd
18 Brooklands Avenue
Cambridge CB2 2HN
Telephone 01223 316644, Fax 01223 313586

CONTENTS

Section 1 Introduction to statistics 1
The mathematics of uncertainty 1
Using statistical methods and techniques 2
Populations and samples 3
Sampling methods 3
Variates or variables 4
Descriptive and inferential statistics 5

Section 2 Frequency distributions 8
Frequency tables 8
Histograms 12
Histograms in relative form 16
Frequency polygons and frequency curves 16
Cumulative frequency diagrams 19
Percentiles, deciles and quartiles 20
Stem and leaf diagrams 22
Box and whisker plots 23

Section 3 Measures of average 30
The arithmetic mean 30
The median 35
The mode 38
Comparing the different measures of average 39
Use of coding and scaling in calculating $\overline{x}$ 40
Weighted averages 41

Section 4 Dispersion 44
The range 44
The standard deviation 45
The interquartile range 52
Skewness 54

Section 5 Probability 60
Trials, sample space and event 60
Events and probabilities 61
Compound events 63
Some useful methods 65
Permutations and combinations 69
Conditional probability and independence 74

Section 6 Random variables 83
Random variables as models 83
Discrete random variables 83
Probability function and cumulative distribution function 86
Continuous random variables 87
The cumulative distribution function 90
Expected value 92
Properties of expectation 95
The variance of X 97
Mode and median for a continuous random variable 100
Combinations of random variables 102

Section 7 Discrete probability distributions 110
The uniform distribution 110
The binomial distribution 110
The Poisson distribution 111
Poisson approximation to the binomial 121

Section 8 Continuous probability distributions 126
The continuous uniform distribution 126
Mean and variance of $X \sim U(a, b)$ 127
The normal distribution 129
Calculation of probabilities 131
The standardised normal distribution 132
Using the normal distribution to approximate the binomial and Poisson 136
Normal approximation to Poisson 139
Linear combinations of independent normal random variables 141

Solutions to exercises 147

Appendix 1 Summary of basic set theory 165

Appendix 2 The normal distribution function 167

Appendix 3 Binomial cumulative distribution function 168

Appendix 4 Poisson cumulative distribution function 169

Permissions

We are grateful to the following examination boards for permission to reproduce questions from past examination papers in the Exercises at the end of each section.

The Associated Examining Board and University of London Examinations and Assessment Council accept no responsibility whatsoever for the accuracy or method of working in the answers given, which are entirely the responsibility of the author.

Associated Examining Board

Section 2: Exercises 7 & 8

Section 4: Exercise 5

Section 5: Exercise 12

Section 7: Exercise 10

Section 8: Exercise 10

University of London Examinations and Assessment Council

Section 1: Exercise 2

Section 2: Exercise 6

Section 4: Exercises 6, 7 & 8

Section 5: Exercises 1, 3, 6, 7, 8, 9, 10 & 11

Section 6: Exercise 4, 7, 9 & 12

Section 7: Exercises 7 & 8

Section 8: Exercises 8 & 9

The tables given in Appendices 2–4 are also reproduced with the kind permission of the University of London Examinations and Assessment Council.

MODULE

T1

Advanced Modular Mathematics

FOREWORD

This book is one of a series covering the University of London Examination and Assessment Council's modular 'A' level Mathematics syllabus. It covers all the subject material for Statistics 1 (Module T1).

While this series of text books has been structured to match the University of London (ULEAC) syllabuses, we hope that the informal style of the text and approach to important concepts will encourage other readers, whose final examinations are from other examination Boards, to use the books for extra reading and practice.

This book is meant to be *used*: read the text, study the worked examples and work through the exercises, which will give you practice in the basic skills you need for maths at this level. There are many books for advanced mathematics, which include many more exercises: use this book to direct your studies, making use of as many other resources as you can. This book will act as a bridge between your new syllabus and the many older books that can still give even more practice in advanced mathematics.

Exercises are given at the end of each section; these range from the basic to exam-type questions. Many exercises, and worked examples, are based on *applications* of the mathematics in this book. We have given answers to all problems, so that you can check your work.

The National Extension College has more experience of flexible-learning materials than any other body (see p. ii). This series is a distillation of that experience: *Advanced Modular Mathematics* helps to put you in control of your own learning.

SECTION

1

Introduction to statistics

INTRODUCTION

This section begins your study of statistics by considering some of the broad principles and applications that are relevant to this area of mathematics. You will be introduced to some of the important terminology and vocabulary that is used in statistical analysis.

At the end of this section you should be able to:

- appreciate the role of statistics in a range of different subject areas
- understand the main terms used in statistics
- describe the difference between the main types of variable
- understand the difference between descriptive and inferential statistics.

The mathematics of uncertainty

In your study of mathematics so far, you will have already developed a number of skills and knowledge relating to a variety of mathematical applications. Virtually all of what you will have met so far relates to such mathematical principles under conditions of certainty. For example, when we examine a situation where $y = 3x^2$, we take it for granted that this relationship is known for certain and will not vary or change at random.

Mathematical statistics recognises that there are areas in mathematics where such relationships and conditions will not always apply – in other words where a degree of *uncertainty* exists. Consider the simple illustration of tossing a coin and noting which side of the coin shows. Clearly, this outcome is not known for certain. We cannot guarantee the result of our action.

Statistics as a subject area is concerned with allowing us to reach conclusions or make decisions in the face of such uncertainty. Naturally, we still wish to apply appropriate mathematical principles and logic to examine such situations. Indeed there is a dual focus throughout the module.

- On the one hand, we shall be *deriving certain key theoretical principles* of mathematical statistics.
- On the other hand, we shall be seeking to *apply these principles* and the theory to a variety of practical situations. Statistics is, above all, an applied discipline.

This section begins by examining the principles whereby we can describe the key features of a set of data that we have obtained. In later sections you will be introduced to a variety of statistical means of achieving this. You will move on to the important area of probability. This is the mechanism whereby we can introduce concepts of uncertainty into our mathematical principles.

Using statistical methods and techniques

Statistical methods and techniques are applicable to a tremendously diverse range of other disciplines. It would a major task to give a realistic picture of the applications that have been made. A few examples will illustrate just how worthwhile the study of statistics is, not just in itself, but also for its relevance to other areas of study.

Typical statistical applications that make use of the topics we shall be covering in this module include:

- Is there any connection between people's social and economic class and their tendency to vote for a particular political party?
- Has the recent TV advertising campaign undertaken by a high street bank been successful in attracting more customers?
- Have the changes introduced in education in terms of the National Curriculum improved student learning?
- Does the treatment for the HIV virus being tested in the laboratory reduce the mortality rate?
- Are more women in favour of legalised abortion than men?
- Has the introduction of lead-free petrol reduced the level of pollution in city centres?

We could extend this list of areas suitable for statistical analysis but those shown illustrate the role that statistics has to play across a range of different subject areas.

From your study of mathematics so far, you will appreciate that mathematics has its own vocabulary and terminology. Statistics is a specialised branch of mathematics and has developed its own vocabulary. In order to proceed, you need to understand the meaning of the more important terms. Further terms will be introduced as and when they are needed.

Populations and samples

In the process of collecting and analysing data we must usually distinguish between a sample and the population. (Note that the word 'population' in statistics does not necessarily refer to people.)

A *population* in statistics refers to the entire set of data that exists.

A *sample*, on the other hand, refers to a carefully chosen and representative part of the population.

This distinction between sample and population is an important one.

Assume that we wish to collect data on family characteristics (sizes, ages, sex, etc.) for the entire country. The population would, therefore, consist of all families in the UK at some moment in time. For a variety of reasons, it would not be realistic to collect such a population data set.

Where a population is large or inaccessible, it is usual to take a sample from the population. We can use the information contained in the sample to make judgements or inferences about the whole population. Naturally we would try to ensure that the sample was representative of the larger group, that is, the population it was meant to represent.

Sometimes we have to use a sampling method because the process of testing destroys the sample. If the official taster in a chocolate bar factory tried every bar, there'd be none left to sell!

You should now try Exercise 1 on page 7.

Sampling methods

In order to obtain information about a population, we usually take a sample and perform certain calculations and tests and then extrapolate back to the population. Often a **random sample** is taken. A random sample is one in which every member of the population has an equal chance of appearing in the sample.

If it is possible to list and give a unique identification to each member of a population, then the list is referred to as a **sampling frame** and the existence of such a frame represents an ideal situation.

The list of members of the population can be mixed thoroughly and the sample drawn randomly. For example, if a survey were being carried out about the chocolate-eating habits of the members of a certain college, then a list could be fairly simply drawn up and names selected randomly for the sample, rather like in a lottery. (A decision would have to be made about whether staff were to be included – this would depend on the purpose of the survey.)

For larger populations, e.g. adults in the United Kingdom, it may be feasible to sample using the Electoral Register, which is effectively a sampling frame for the voting population. However, it will not include all adults in the United Kingdom and can never be completely up to date.

For surveys on large populations it is common practice to conduct a **pilot study** first to ensure that sensible responses are obtained and that all of the information required is being obtained.

There are many other methods of sampling available to statisticians, but these are not part of 'A' level statistics.

You should now be able to try Exercise 2 on page 7.

Variates or variables

We frequently use the term '**variable**' or '**variate**' when dealing with statistical data (the two terms are effectively interchangeable). Assume that we are conducting an investigation into the sizes of families in the UK. For each family in the investigation we could collect data on such things as:

- the number of people in the family group
- their ages
- their educational background
- which part of the country they live in

and so on. Each of these characteristics is a variable or variate in our investigation. Simply, a variable refers to a characteristic, feature or factor that takes different values in the data set.

A variable will fall into one of three general categories. It may be:

- discrete
- continuous
- qualitative.

To explain each of three categories:

- A **discrete variable** is one which can only have certain numbers (or take certain fixed values). If the variable were the number of people in a family, it would be an example of a discrete variable. The number of people might be 1 or 2 or 3, for example, but it could not possibly be 1.4 or 5.3. Don't assume that a discrete variable can only take integer values. Shoe sizes, for example, are discrete – 7, $7\frac{1}{2}$, 8, $8\frac{1}{2}$, etc.
- A **continuous variable** is one which can take any numerical value within a given range. Imagine that we want to extend our

investigation of families to look at diet patterns: we might want to analyse the weight of family members. This would be an example of a continuous variable, since, technically, we could measure this variable to any degree of accuracy that we wanted. We might, for example, measure the variable to the nearest kilogram, to the nearest gram, or to the nearest milligram.

- **Qualitative variables** are those that cannot be shown in terms of numbers. For example, suppose our chosen variable was the sex of the family members. We cannot express this variable sensibly as a number – we would probably record the data collected as 'male' or 'female'. (However, for statistical analysis, we might convert such a variable into number form – e.g. letting male = 0 and female = 1 – but such numbers have no meaning in the normal sense.)

It is also conventional to distinguish between variables relating to a population and those relating to a sample. Although we have yet to introduce the topic, you will be aware of the statistic generally referred to as the 'average': suppose we had calculated an average for the height of a group of people. This group might be a sample or it might be a statistical population. It is conventional to represent such a statistic referring to a population with a symbol from the Greek alphabet, and those referring to a sample with a character from the normal alphabet. You will meet these symbols as we progress.

You should now be able to try Exercise 3 on page 7.

Descriptive and inferential statistics

The final piece of vocabulary that we need to introduce at this stage relates to the difference between descriptive and inferential statistics.

- **Descriptive statistics** as a subject is concerned with the techniques for collecting, grouping, summarising and presenting data: techniques which allow us to describe the main features of a set of data.

  Returning to our sample of families, we might use such techniques to describe statistically the number of families in the sample that consist entirely of people over the age of 60.

- **Inferential statistics** is concerned with trying to reach a conclusion on a population when only a sample is available. Typically, inferential statistics is concerned with reaching conclusions about some characteristic of the population based on the descriptive statistics of the sample.

  So, for example, we would try and determine how many families in the entire statistical population consisted of people over the age of 60, based only on the sample.

Inferential statistical methods become important because it is the population that we normally wish to examine. However, as it is usually only a sample for which we actually have data, we need to be able to move from sample to population with a reasonable degree of certainty.

The following sections of this module begin by examining methods suitable for descriptive statistical analysis. We then examine probability and the role it plays in linking descriptive to inferential statistics. The final sections deal with random variables and their probability distributions. A random variable is a quantity which can take a range of values (discrete or continuous) where each of these values occurs with a certain probability. Random variables provide us with the link between 'pure' probability theory and 'applied' statistics.

As an illustration of the general processes involved in a statistical investigation, consider the following example.

Example

A manufacturer of batteries claims that his particular brand will remain usable for at least 1000 hours.

It is decided to check his claim and an independent observer takes a sample from his production line and conducts an experiment. He runs the batteries until they are dead and notes the time for each. This is a random or unpredictable quantity – an example of a continuous variable.

Having collected his data, he will then perform some calculations and produce some graphical illustrations of his results. He will attempt to model his data by a probability distribution (some of these distributions are discussed in Sections 7 and 8).

Finally, he will use his results to try to draw some conclusions about the manufacturer's claim – he will test a hypothesis about its validity.

This procedure is summarised in Figure 1.1

Figure 1.1

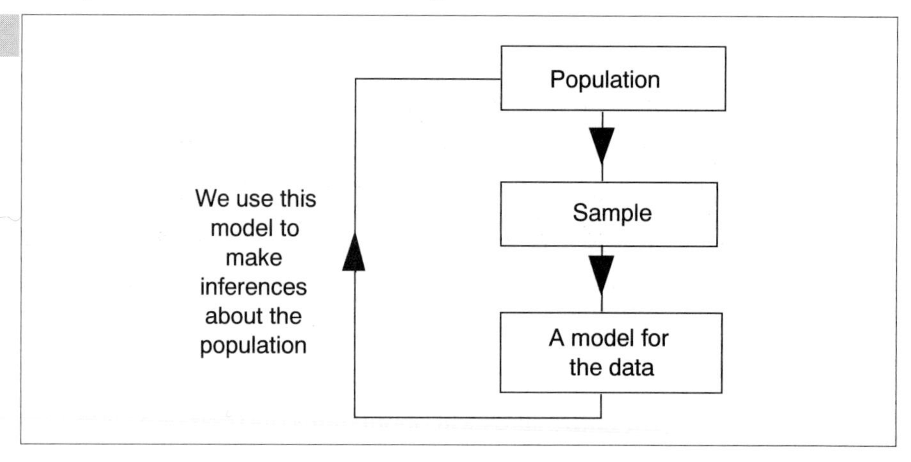

EXERCISES

1 What reasons can you think of which would prohibit the collection of all data for all families in the UK?

2 (a) Explain briefly:

(i) why it is often desirable to take samples

(ii) what you understand by a sampling frame.

(b) Give an example of a sample frame suitable for use in a survey of attitudes of pupils in a school to a proposal to start the school day 15 minutes earlier.

3 For each of the following statistical variables, state whether it is discrete, continuous or qualitative:

(a) your height

(b) the colour of your hair

(c) the number of people in your family group

(d) the number of exam passes you have already

(e) the time taken for the 08.15 from Liverpool Street Station to reach Chelmsford

(f) the weight of a bag of flour.

SUMMARY

In this section you have taken a broad look at the subject of statistics. As well as considering the various applications of statistics in a range of different fields, you have been introduced to some of the basic terminology and vocabulary that you will meet and use in the rest of your work on module T1.

Now you have completed this section you should appreciate how:

- statistics has a role to play in many other disciplines
- variables fall into one of three types: discrete, continuous or qualitative
- data may relate to a statistical population or to only part of that population, i.e. a sample
- statistical methods generally relate either to descriptive or to inferential statistics.

SECTION

2

Frequency distributions

INTRODUCTION

In this section we look at the method of tabulating data in the form of a frequency table and at methods of presenting such data in diagrammatic form.

At the end of this section you should be able to:

- construct a frequency table from raw data
- construct a histogram
- deal with open-ended intervals
- deal with unequal intervals
- draw a frequency polygon
- calculate cumulative frequencies
- construct a cumulative frequency polygon
- identify percentiles, deciles and quartiles on the cumulative frequency polygon.
- draw and interpret stem and leaf diagrams
- draw and interpret box and whisker plots.

Frequency tables

We shall illustrate and develop the appropriate statistical techniques with reference to the two data sets shown below in Tables 2.1 and 2.2.

Table 2.1 **Height of 50 adult males, measured in cm**

168.3	169.1	175.9	178.8	172.3	182.9	173.9	184.1	168.9	178.1
175.2	167.7	169.3	189.8	179.7	187.9	160.6	171.3	159.8	167.2
195.3	166.5	164.8	173.3	175.0	178.1	172.3	172.5	183.5	171.0
163.0	169.1	172.4	182.4	172.3	172.1	180.1	175.2	183.4	170.5
175.0	184.2	183.2	176.2	171.5	175.0	178.1	175.1	181.0	178.1

Table 2.2 **Heights of 50 adult females, measured in cm**

168.8	168.8	170.8	166.2	169.8	170.1	171.6	171.6	153.3	161.1
172.1	171.3	172.1	163.4	171.8	163.2	168.5	169.0	169.1	175.2
154.8	159.9	181.9	155.8	166.2	156.1	169.6	163.7	171.3	173.9
172.8	159.9	166.2	170.6	172.4	169.8	167.3	177.4	159.6	170.3
172.9	162.8	162.1	159.4	161.9	157.1	161.7	164.7	162.2	169.8

We shall be using these data sets to illustrate a number of key statistical concepts in this and subsequent sections, so it is worthwhile describing them in detail.

We have taken a sample of 50 adult males and 50 adult females and measured their heights (in centimetres, correct to one decimal place). We can easily imagine a study that we may be involved in where we have to compare heights of males and females in order to ascertain similarities and differences between the two sexes. The study might be for medical or health purposes, for some business organisation, for the police or armed forces and so on.

With the data in the form given, it is difficult to draw any conclusions about the heights of adults.

We cannot readily identify the key features of the two data sets. For the data to be useful it has to be put into a more manageable form. The first step in this process is often to construct a **frequency table**.

A frequency table for males is shown in Table 2.3, where the letter x is used to stand for the variable 'height' and the letter f is used to stand for the 'frequency'.

Table 2.3 **Frequency table for male heights (cm)**

height (x)	frequency (f)
155–	1
160–	3
165–	8
170–	12
175–	14
180–	9
185–	2
190–	0
195–	1
200–	0
Total frequency	50

Here the interval '155–', for example, is to be interpreted as $155 \le x < 160$.

Note that an extra interval '200–' is included at the end to indicate that the previous interval stops at 200 and is therefore the same width as the earlier intervals.

We can now pick out some general features of the distribution:

- No one is less than 155 cm.
- No one is above 200 cm.
- Most males are between 170 and 180 cm.

Stages in constructing a frequency table

Step 1: From the raw data, determine the minimum and maximum values.

The difference between the two is known as the *range*. This allows us to see the range of data the table will have to deal with.

The lowest height in Table 2.1 is 159.8 and the largest is 195.3, so the table must encompass a range of about 40 cm. (As with many statistical methods it is useful to round numbers to some manageable and meaningful figure.)

Step 2: Choose the number of intervals to be shown in the table.

There is no absolute rule that can be applied, but we use our own common sense and, through trial and error, produce a table which looks appropriate for the data. It is conventional to have between 5 and 15 intervals in such a table, with fewer intervals for small data sets than for large. If there are too few intervals then important details about the data set may be lost as we aggregate the data. On the other hand, with too many intervals the data may be insufficiently aggregated and no patterns in the data will be apparent.

Step 3: Decide how large each interval should be.

In Table 2.3 the intervals are all 5 cm. Steps 2 and 3 are related and we must choose interval sizes and the number of intervals together. If possible, we should choose intervals which are all the same width. Here, a choice of 5 cm provides us with a sensible interval size and also gives nine intervals, which seems appropriate.

Step 4: Ensure that the boundaries of the intervals are clear and unambiguous.

In Table 2.3 the intervals are expressed so that there is no possible misunderstanding. If we had shown the intervals as:

155 to 160 cm
160 to 165 cm
165 to 170 cm etc.

then when we aggregate the raw data we are uncertain whether to place an observation of, say, 160 in the first interval or in the second.

Step 5: Work through the data set allocating each observation to the appropriate interval.

Class boundaries

The data in Tables 2.1 and 2.2 was given correction to one decimal place. The first item in Table 2.1, namely 168.3, could therefore have been a measurement anywhere in the interval $168.25 \le x < 168.35$ since any measurement within this interval would round to 168.3 to one decimal place.

When the data is grouped into the frequency table, Table 2.3, the true limits of the intervals are therefore slightly different. The true limits of each interval are called the **class boundaries**.

As an example, consider the class 160– (i.e. $160 \le x < 165$). Strictly speaking, any height in the interval $159.95 \le x < 164.95$ would end up in this class and therefore these extremes determine the class more precisely.

You should now be able to do Exercise 1 on page 27.

Other types of frequency table

It is quite common, and frequently useful, to show a frequency distribution in terms of **relative** and **cumulative** *frequencies* as well as in absolute terms. Table 2.4 shows these for males.

Table 2.4 Frequency table for males showing relative and cumulative frequencies

Heights (cm) x	*Frequency* f	*Relative frequency*	*Cumulative frequency*
155–	1	0.02	1
160–	3	0.06	4
165–	8	0.16	12
170–	12	0.24	24
175–	14	0.28	38
180–	9	0.18	47
185–	2	0.04	49
190–	0	0.00	49
195–	1	0.02	50
200–	0	0.00	50
Total	50	1.00	50

- The cumulative frequencies show the number of observations *up to and including that interval*; so, for example, there were 24 males who had heights up to, but not including, 175 cm.
- Relative frequencies are useful for comparing distributions of data with probability distributions. They are simply calculated as:

  frequency ÷ total frequency

  So, for example, for the interval 160– with frequency $f = 3$, the relative frequency is $3 \div 50 = 0.06$.

  Note that relative frequencies should always add up to 1 (with allowances made for rounding).

You should now be able to do Exercise 2 on page 27.

Histograms

Whilst frequency tables are a useful first step in describing some set of data, a visual presentation of the frequency table can be even more useful. The diagram of a frequency table is known as a **histogram**. Figure 2.1 shows a histogram for the height of males shown in Table 2.3.

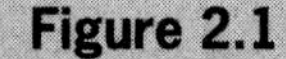

Figure 2.1

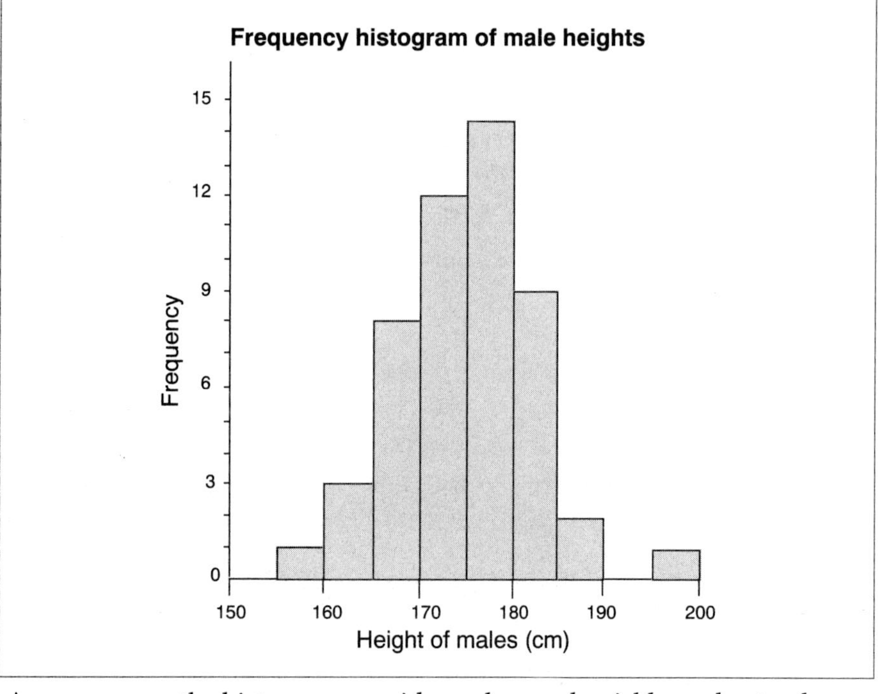

As you can see the histogram provides a clear and quickly understood picture of the pattern of the variable. The saying: 'a picture is worth a thousand words' is as true in statistics as elsewhere. We gain an immediate overall impression of the frequency distribution from the histogram.

Histograms are quite easy to construct. The variable we are analysing – height of males – is shown on the horizontal axis and the frequencies are shown on the vertical axis. Naturally, we must exercise all the usual caution when drawing such a diagram: ensuring that the scales are appropriate, titles and labels are clearly shown and so on. Note also that a histogram has the columns joined together, corresponding to the continuous nature of the data being illustrated. Where there is a 'gap' between columns, as there is in Figure 2.1, this is not a gap at all, rather an interval with zero frequency.

You should now be able to attempt Exercise 3 on page 27.

Problems encountered in constructing a histogram

Constructing a histogram from a frequency table is usually straightforward, but there are two aspects that we need to be aware of.

Open-ended intervals

These are intervals which have no upper (or lower) limit specified. In Table 2.3 assume that we had one interval where heights were defined as less than 160 cm rather than 155– or $155 \leq x < 160$. This would be an open-ended interval given that we had not specified an exact lower limit.

Equally, we could have an upper open-ended interval. This causes some difficulty when drawing the histogram as we do not know where to draw the lower (or upper) limit for the appropriate bar in the diagram. Typically we might use such open-ended intervals if we had relatively few observations scattered across several intervals at one end of the distribution.

Conventionally, we can deal with such open-ended intervals in one of two ways.

- We could give this interval the same width as the interval next to it. Here we would assume a lower limit of 155 for this open-ended interval so that this gives us an interval which has the same width (of 5 cm) as all our other intervals.
- There may be a logical limit implied in the data. Assume, for example, that we had constructed a frequency table showing the distribution of the ages of a sample of people. One group might be those who are 'under 5 years old'. We could realistically assume a lower limit of 0 for such an interval.

Unequal intervals

The second potential problem occurs when we have a frequency table where the intervals are not all of the same width. Because intervals may be of different widths, we need to compare not only the height of each bar but also its width relative to the others. In other words, in a histogram we are actually comparing areas (Height × Width = Area). To illustrate, let us examine Table 2.5.

Table 2.5 **Frequency table for males (amended)**

Height (cm) x	*Frequency f*
155–	1
160–	3
165–	8
170–	12
175–	14
180–	9
185–	3
200–	0
Total	50

Table 2.5 shows male heights but with three intervals from Table 2.3 amalgamated into one (185–, 190– and 195–). The histogram we might at first consider for such a table is shown in Figure 2.2.

Figure 2.2

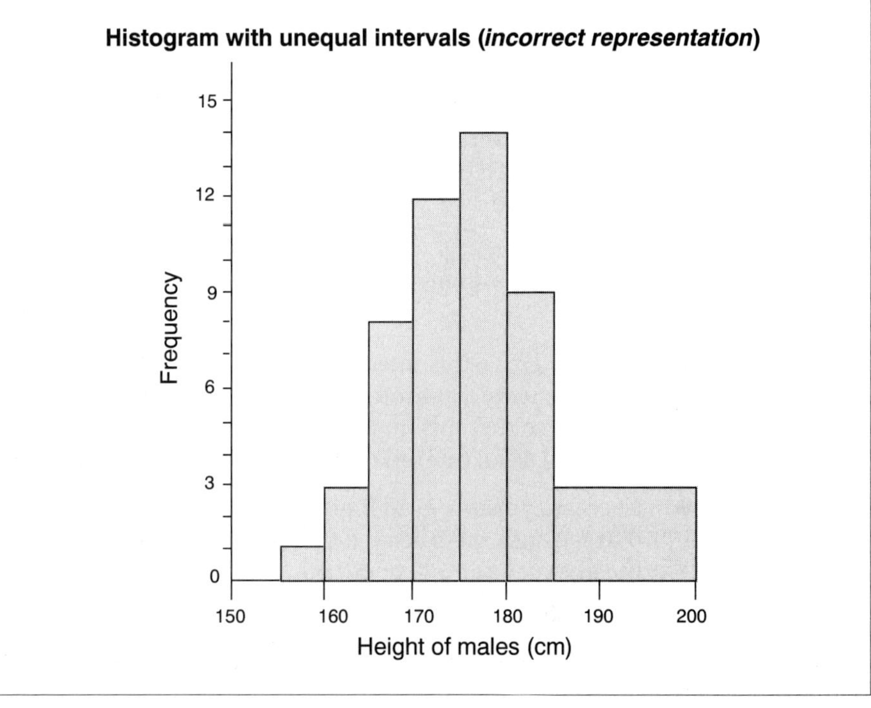

On reflection, however, it is clear that we now gain a distorted view of the last interval. Whilst the number of males (three) in this interval is the same as that for the interval 160– , the histogram gives the impression that there is more data in the interval 185– than in the interval 160–. It is clear that in drawing the histogram properly we must adjust the diagram to allow for the extra width of this interval; we need to scale the frequency of that interval *downward* to bring it into line with our standard interval width.

Conversely, if an interval were smaller than usual, we would scale the frequency upwards. The idea is that the area of each column represents the frequency of that class – i.e. the number of items in it. To achieve this, we re-label the vertical axis as 'frequency density' and decide the height of each column as $\dfrac{\text{frequency}}{\text{class width}}$.

Figure 2.3

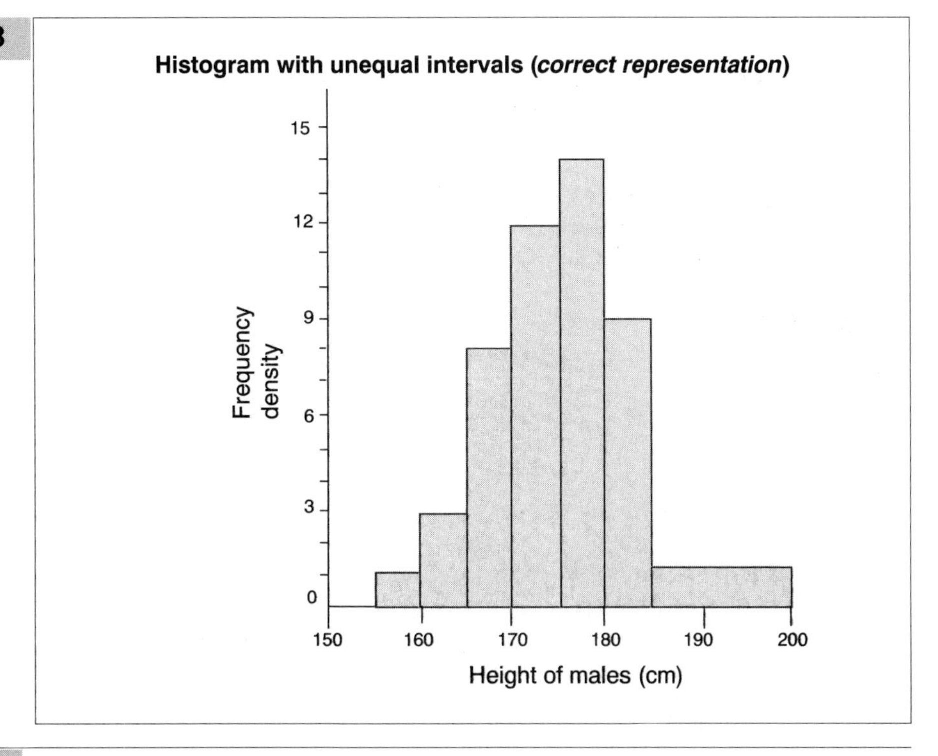

Example Find the areas of the intervals $160 \leq x < 165$ and $185 \leq x < 200$

Solution

Interval	Width	Height	Area
$160 \leq x < 165$	5	3	15
$185 \leq x < 200$	15	1	15

Note that this result is to be expected as these intervals have equal frequencies.

Histograms in relative form

Histograms may also be constructed to show relative, rather than absolute, frequencies. This is often useful where we wish to compare two or more data sets of differing sizes. If the sample of males had been of 500 whilst that of females was 350 then a histogram of absolute frequencies would be unhelpful, because there were more males than females in the data set. A histogram of *relative frequencies* would make comparison and analysis easier. The only difference in its construction is that the vertical scale will now run from 0 to 1 (or from 0 to 100 if we are showing percentages).

Frequency polygons and frequency curves

We may construct a **frequency polygon** from a frequency table. Such a diagram is constructed in much the same way as a histogram. We join the *midpoint* of each interval (i.e. the midpoint of the top of each column) together with a straight line. The appropriate diagram for heights of males is shown in Figure 2.4.

Figure 2.4

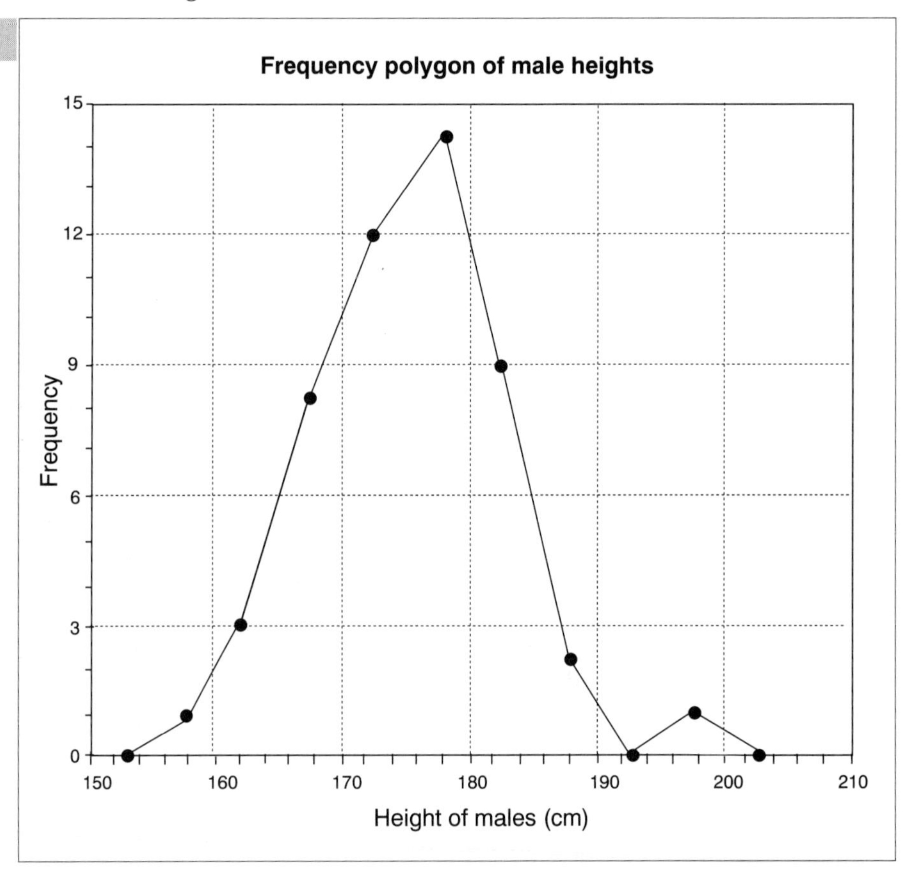

Each point plotted represents the midpoint of an interval. Note that at each end of the polygon we have plotted a point on the horizontal axis representing where the midpoint of the next interval would have been.

The reason for using midpoints is that this ensures that the total area under the polygon is equal to the corresponding area plotted in the histogram. The frequency polygon is particularly useful for showing the general shape of the distribution and for comparing two or more such distributions on the same diagram.

If we now draw a similar diagram for heights of females superimposed on Figure 2.4 we obtain Figure 2.5 where comparison between the two is now much simpler.

Figure 2.5

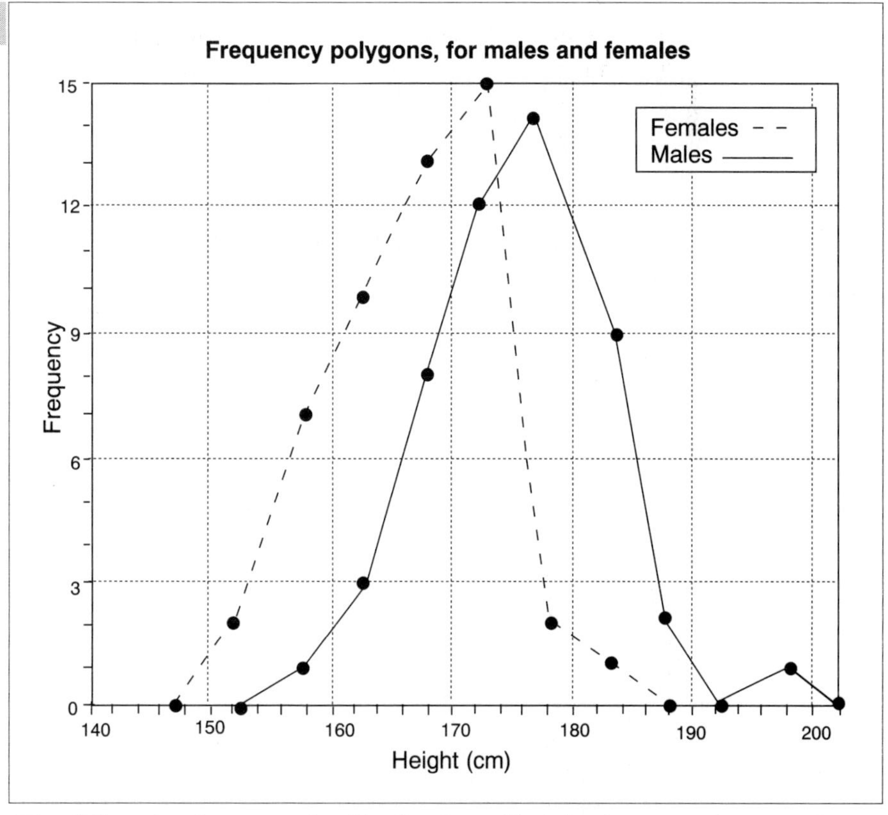

The differences between the distribution of heights between the sexes is now immediately apparent.

Frequency polygons are derived from histograms. If the data you begin with is grouped in intervals of unequal widths, then (just like with a histogram) the vertical axis will need to be 'frequency density'.

The rule, therefore, is: set up the axes just as if you were going to draw the histogram.

Frequency curves

You will remember that in Section 1 we distinguished between samples and populations. The data that we have analysed has been sample data, and the frequency polygon is technically the shape of the distribution of the sample data. Frequently we may wish to infer the general shape of the population distribution. We achieve this by constructing a **frequency curve** rather than a polygon. This is done by smoothing the polygon.

The logic behind this is simple. Because we are dealing with sample data, we may encounter slight discrepancies in the sample distribution which we would not expect in the population. A smoothing process removes these.

Let us return to Figure 2.4 to illustrate the process. If we examine the right-hand side of the polygon we see that it dips to zero for the interval $190 \leq x < 195$ and then rises again in the successive interval. It would be illogical to suppose that in the statistical population there was no one in this height group, but that there were people in the next. The plausible reason for such a dip lies with the fact that we have only a sample of the population. We can realistically assume there to be a slight discrepancy between the observed sample data and the expected population profile. The frequency curve smooths the dip out, as in Figure 2.6.

Figure 2.6

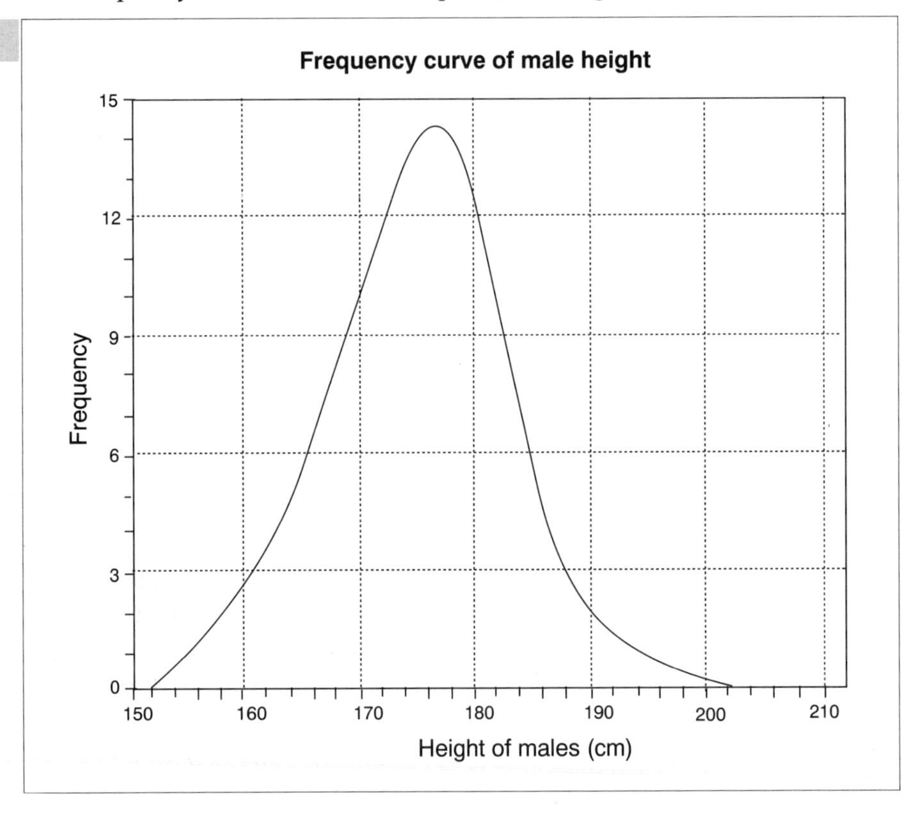

Cumulative frequency diagrams

Up to now we have looked at frequency tables to see how many observations fall into a particular interval. It is often useful to present the corresponding diagram showing cumulative frequencies.

The **cumulative frequency polygon** is drawn by plotting the cumulative frequency at each interval against the *upper limit* of the interval (along the horizontal axis). The points are then joined together with straight lines. Figure 2.7 shows the cumulative frequency polygon for males. (Compare this with the cumulative frequency table for males, shown in Table 2.4.)

Figure 2.7

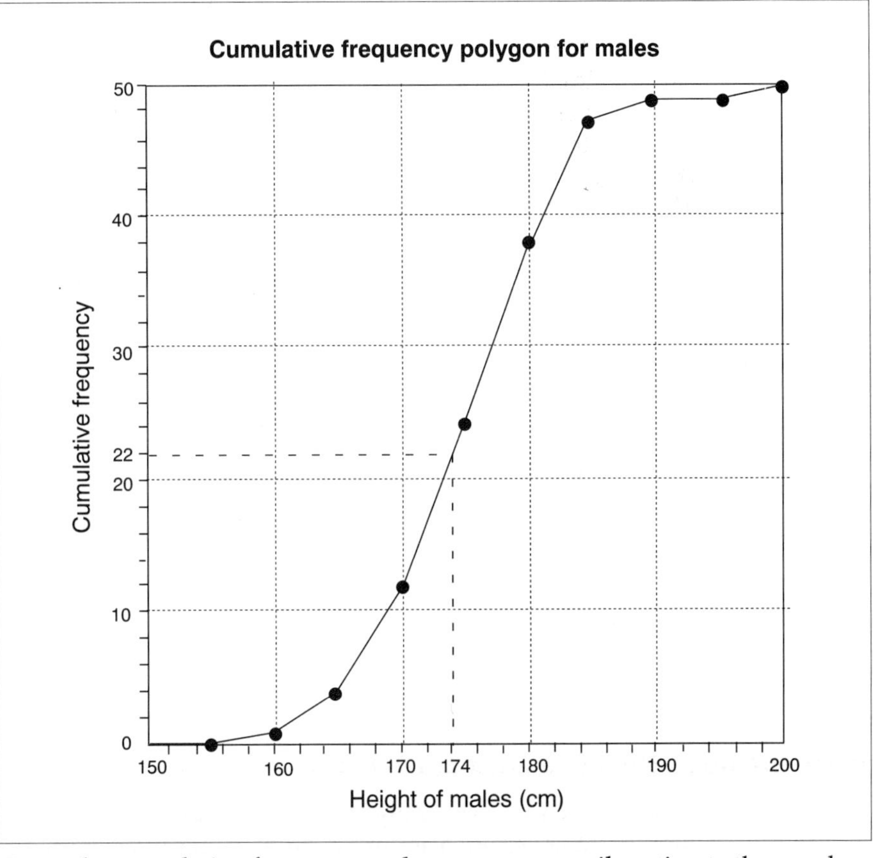

From the cumulative frequency polygon we can easily estimate the number of observations falling below (or above) a particular value. This is done by simply reading the cumulative frequency at the point of the polygon with that value. This gives the number of observations below the value. The number above it is obtained by subtracting this from the total number.

For example, suppose that we wished to estimate the proportion of males with a height less than 174 cm. Given that this value is not consistent with the intervals we have used we must estimate from the cumulative frequency polygon. We see that approximately 44% (22/50) males are below this height.

If we now draw the cumulative frequency polygon for female heights superimposed on Figure 2.7 we obtain Figure 2.8 and we can read from this that approximately 88% (44/50) of females are below a height of 174 cm, for example.

Figure 2.8

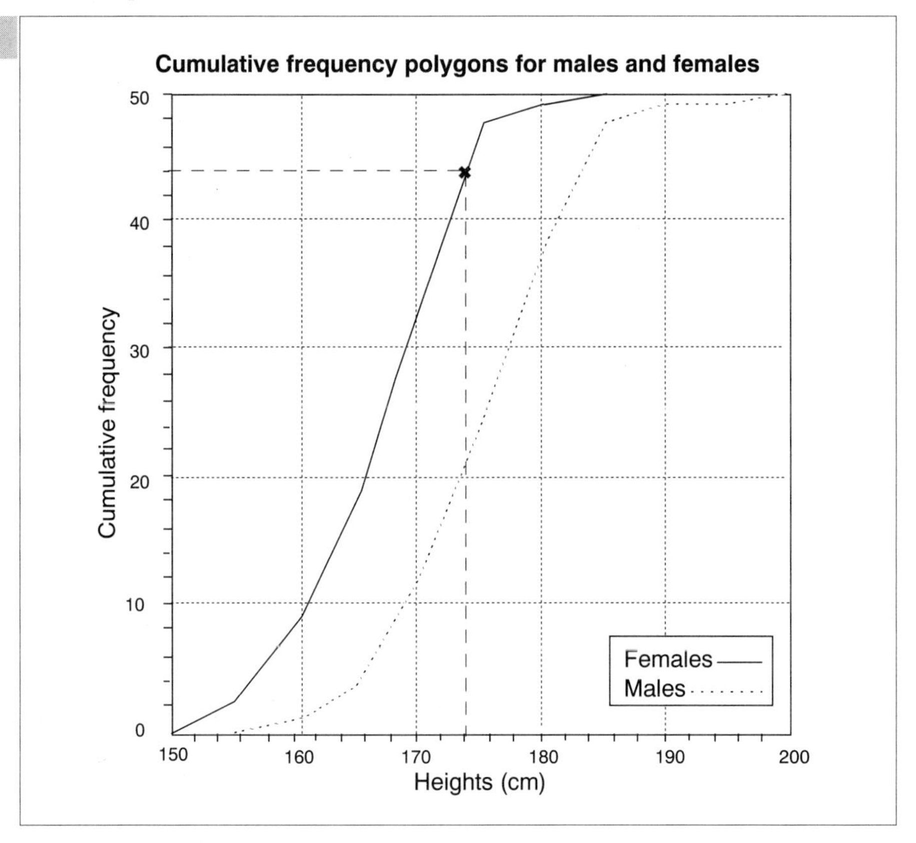

Percentiles, deciles and quartiles

Cumulative frequency polygons may also be constructed to show relative or percentage frequencies in exactly the same way as histograms. Such diagrams would show the percentage of observations falling below a specified value. It is useful when comparing two or more data sets where the total frequencies differ.

However, such percentage cumulative frequency polygons allow us to determine **percentile, decile** and **quartile** values of a data set. To see what these mean let us examine Figure 2.9 which shows the cumulative percentage frequencies for males.

Figure 2.9

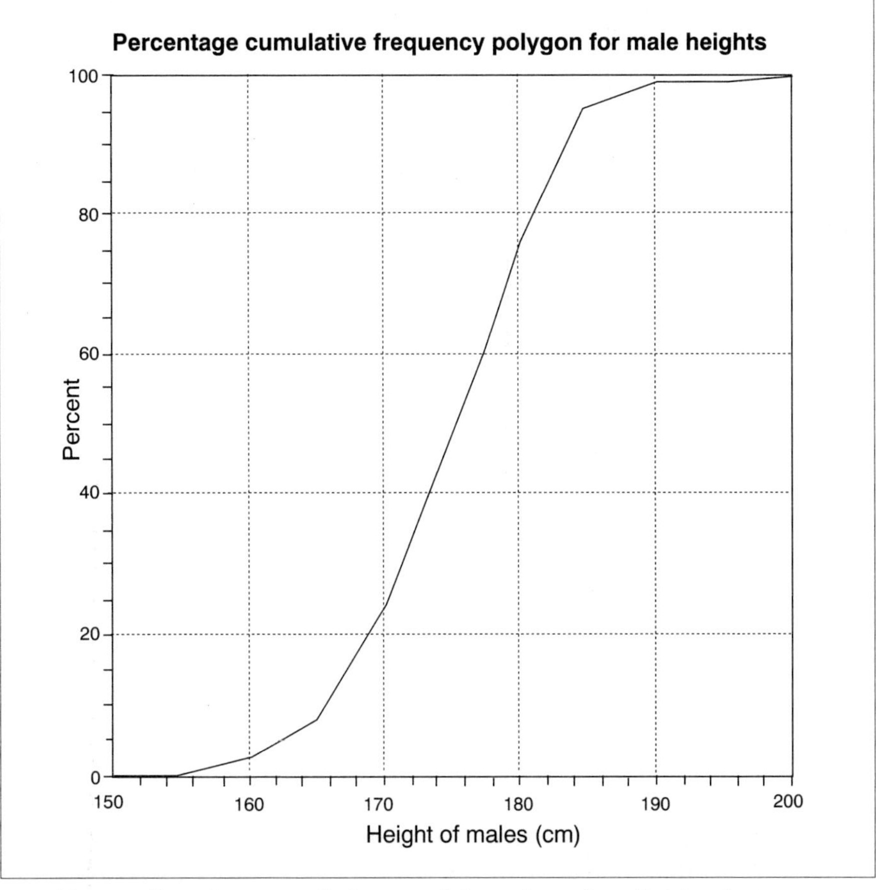

- **Percentile** – A percentile is one of the values that divides the distribution into 100 equal parts. For example, we might find the fifth percentile. This would be the value for the variable such that 5% of observations fell below this value and 95% above. The 95th percentile would be the reverse of this: 95% of observations would fall below and 5% above.

- **Decile** – Where the chosen percentile coincides with multiples of 10 (10%, 20%, 30%, etc) then the value is known instead as a decile, e.g. the 30th percentile is called the 3rd decile.

- **Quartile** – Finally, where the data is divided not into percentages or into tenths, but rather into quarters, we refer to the quartiles (corresponding to the 25%, 50% and 75% points of the percentage cumulative frequency). The second quartile (Q_2) is the median. The other two (Q_1 and Q_3) are known as the **upper** and **lower quartiles.**

Example Using the cumulative frequency polygon of Figure 2.9 find the following:

(a) the fifth percentile
(b) the 95th percentile
(c) the first decile (10%)
(d) the upper quartile (75%)

Solution The approximate answers from the diagram are:

(a) 162 cm
(b) 184 cm
(c) 166 cm
(d) 180 cm

The interpretation of these values is straightforward. The first decile, for example, indicates that 10% of adult males are below a height of 166 cm (and conversely 90% are above this height). Naturally such a statement is strictly true only for the sample data we are analysing; but, if we are confident that the sample is representative of the statistical population, we could reasonably infer that the same would be true of all adult males. Equally, we could use such statistics to compare adult males with adult females. You may wish to do this by yourself as a final exercise for this section.

It should be noted that the percentiles can also be obtained directly from the cumulative frequency polygon. Figure 2.7 illustrates how one might go about finding the 44th percentile. Since the last number of items of data is 50, the 44th percentile will be found by reading at $\frac{44}{100} \times 50 = 22$ on the vertical axis, giving

44th percentile = 174 cm

Stem and leaf diagrams

Stem and leaf diagrams provide a convenient way of representing discrete data. Suppose, for example, that we asked a group of 20 students how many TV programmes they had watched during the previous week. Let's suppose their answers were:

39, 11, 12, 24, 25, 44, 8, 28, 15, 26, 32, 21, 5, 12, 24, 28, 13, 21, 15, 28

A neat way of presenting these results diagrammatically is to draw a **stem and leaf diagram**.

Begin by drawing a vertical line and, on the left hand side, mark the rows 0 (for single figures), 1 (for tens), 2 (for twenties), 3 (for thirties) and so on.

0	
1	
2	
3	
4	

Now place the twenty readings in the appropriate row:

0	8	5							
1	11	12	15	12	13	15			
2	24	25	28	26	21	24	28	21	28
3	39	32							
4	44								

Finally, rearrange the numbers so that they are in order and only the second digit is recorded.

0	5	8							
1	1	2	2	3	5	5			
2	1	1	4	4	5	6	8	8	8
3	2	9							
4	4								

(Thus, for example, each 8 in row 2 stands for 28 and the 9 in row 3 stands for 39.)

The above final diagram is called a stem and leaf diagram. It shows very neatly how the figures are spread out.

You should now be able to attempt Exercise 4 on page 27.

Box and whisker plots

Box and whisker plots provide a convenient way of representing the range, together with the median and quartiles. They can be used for both continuous and discrete data.

For example, look again at Figure 2.9. From this we can see that:

- The minimum reading is 155 cm and the maximum is 200 cm.
- The lower (or first) quartile is approximately 170 cm.
- The median is approximately 176 cm.
- The upper (or third) quartile is approximately 180 cm.

A neat way of presenting these results diagrammatically is to draw a box and whisker plot.

Begin by drawing a vertical line and, having chosen a suitable scale, mark in the median and quartiles.

Figure 2.10

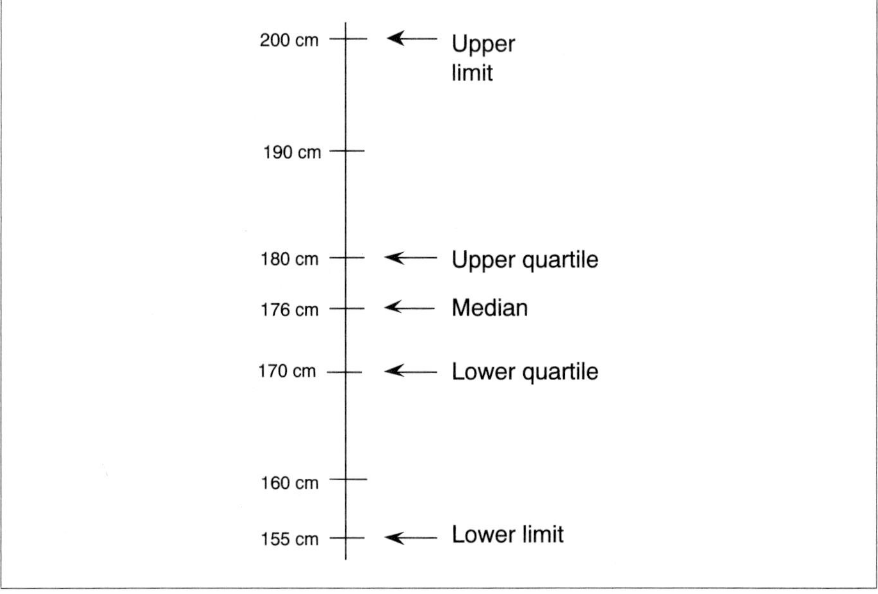

Now draw a box going from the lower to the upper quartile and mark in the median with a line across the box. This box represents the middle half of the distribution. Now draw lines out from the box to the extreme values. These lines (or 'whiskers') represent the lower and upper quarters of the distribution. Their chief purpose is to show the positions of the extreme values.

Figure 2.11

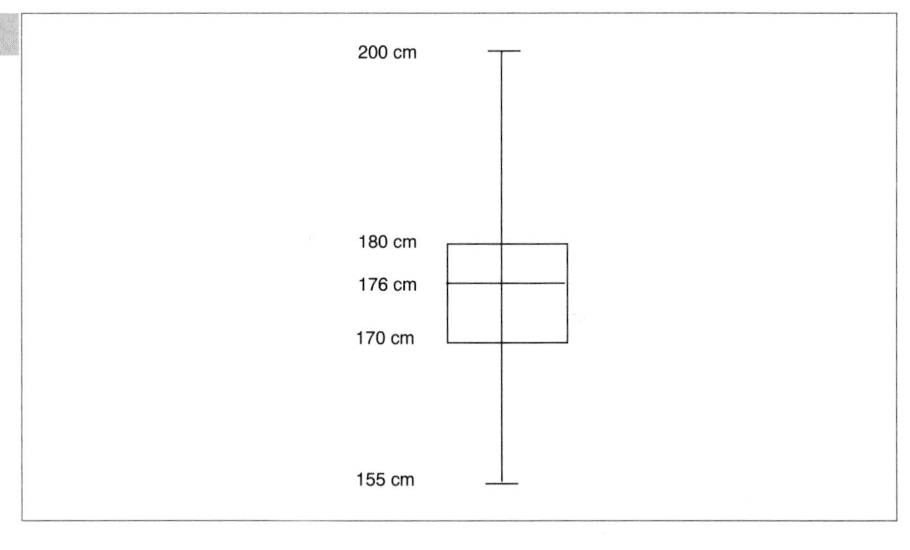

The final diagram is called a box and whisker plot. It shows very neatly how the figures are spread out and how the middle 50% are clustered.

Suppose we were given the box and whisker plot in Figure 2.12.

Figure 2.12

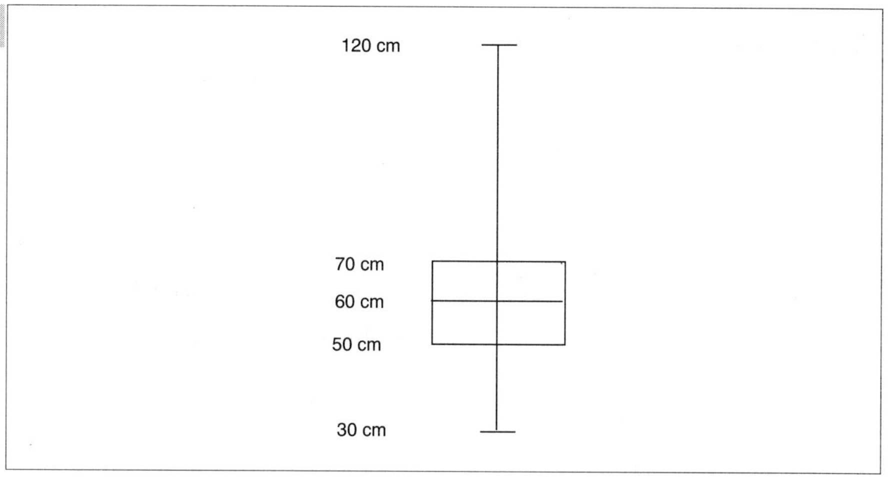

How might we interpret this summarised version of what may have been a large data set? Firstly, most of the data is concentrated around the interval 50 cm to 70 cm (i.e. 50% is included between the upper and lower quartiles). Secondly the range is 120–30 = 90 cm.

However the data clearly does not lie symmetrically within this range. The fact that the median is halfway between the lower and upper quartiles does suggest symmetry, however. We would be forced to conclude in this case that there are one or more items of data in the set which are extreme values and are atypical of the data set in general. Such atypical members of a data set are called **outliers**, and a box and whisker plot correctly interpreted can provide evidence of these.

Example

An evening class in GCSE maths is mainly intended for people who have recently taken GCSE at school and want a better grade, but it's attended by a wider selection of people than that. Here is a summary of their ages.

Age (x)	Frequency (f)
15–16	2
17–19	10
20–25	6
26–35	7

Draw a histogram for this data.

Solution

The first thing we must do is to think about the age figures. Age is a continuous variable, but the class intervals in this example are written as for a discrete variable, i.e. 15–16 and then 17–19, with no mention of anything between 16 and 17.

This is because the age is counted here (in the usual way) in *completed years*. This behaves very much like a discrete variable (so there is no age between 16 and 17) even though it is measuring something which varies continuously.

To draw the histogram, we must first calculate the class widths and then the frequency densities.

Age x	*Frequency f*	*Class width*	*Frequency density (= frequency/class width)*
15–16	2	17 – 15 = 2*	2/2 = 1
17–19	10	20 – 17 = 3	10/3 = 3.3
20–25	6	26 – 20 = 6	6/6 = 1
26–35	7	36 – 26 = 10	7/10 = 0.7

*The class width is the 'distance' between successive lower class boundaries – here, 17 – 15 = 2. This corresponds to people with ages 15 and 16, covering a range of two years. For the highest class, we imagine that the first empty class begins at 36.

Figure 2.13

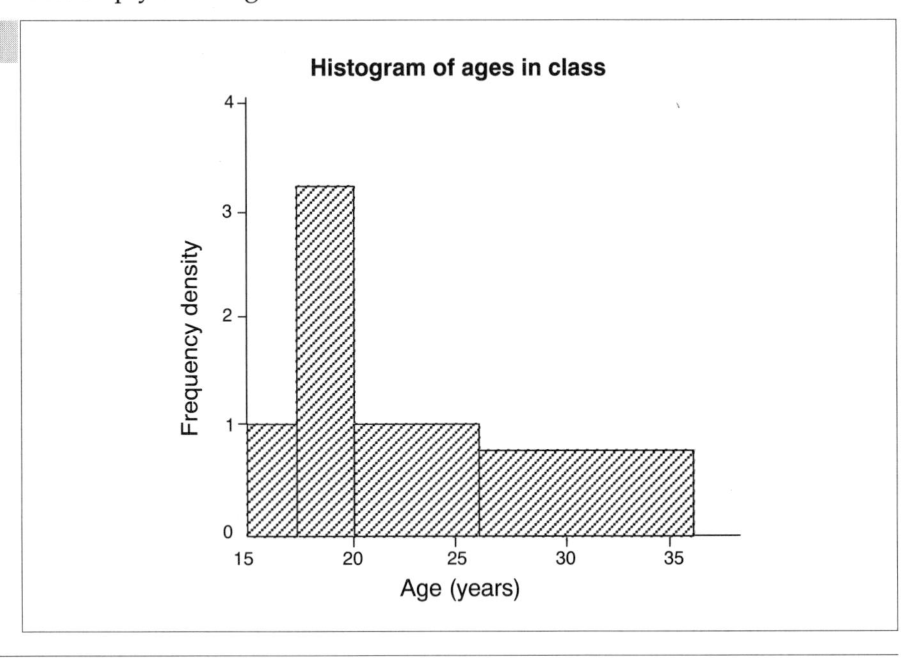

You should now be able to attempt Exercises 5 to 8 on pages 27–29.

EXERCISES

1 Produce a frequency table for Table 2.2 using the intervals given below:

Heights, cm	*Number of females*
150–	
155–	
160–	
165–	
170–	
175–	
180–	
185–	
Total frequency	50

2 Construct a table like Table 2.4 for females.

3 Construct a comparable histogram for females, using your frequency table from Exercise 1.

4 Draw stem and leaf diagrams to represent the following data:

(a) 2, 6, 12, 12, 15, 18, 20, 20, 27, 31, 38, 42

(b) 4.8, 1.8, 3.0, 3.4, 1.2, 0.9, 3.3, 2.8, 2.3, 0.5, 2.2, 2.9, 3.7, 2.1, 4.2, 1.0, 2.5, 1.5, 1.6, 3.2

5 Using Figure 2.8, estimate the lowest and highest values, quartiles and median for females. Hence represent the data with a box and whisker plot. (You should use the same scales as for the males on page 24.) Comment on any difference between the male and female distributions.

6 Telephone calls arriving at a switchboard are answered by the telephonist. The following table shows the time, to the nearest second, recorded as being taken by the telephonist to answer the calls received during one day.

Time to answer (to nearest second)	Number of calls
10–19	20
20–24	20
25–29	15
30	14
31–34	16
35–39	10
40–59	10

Represent these data by a histogram.

Give a reason to justify the use of a histogram to represent these data.

7 At a health centre, where all the consultations are by appointment, a survey of 300 such appointments revealed that 265 were delayed. The times, in minutes, of these delays are summarised in the following table.

Delay, x minutes	Number of appointments
$0 < x < 1$	34
$1 \leq x < 3$	50
$3 \leq x < 5$	36
$5 \leq x < 10$	65
$10 \leq x < 15$	45
$15 \leq x < 20$	15
$20 \leq x < 30$	20

The illustration below was used in the report of the survey.

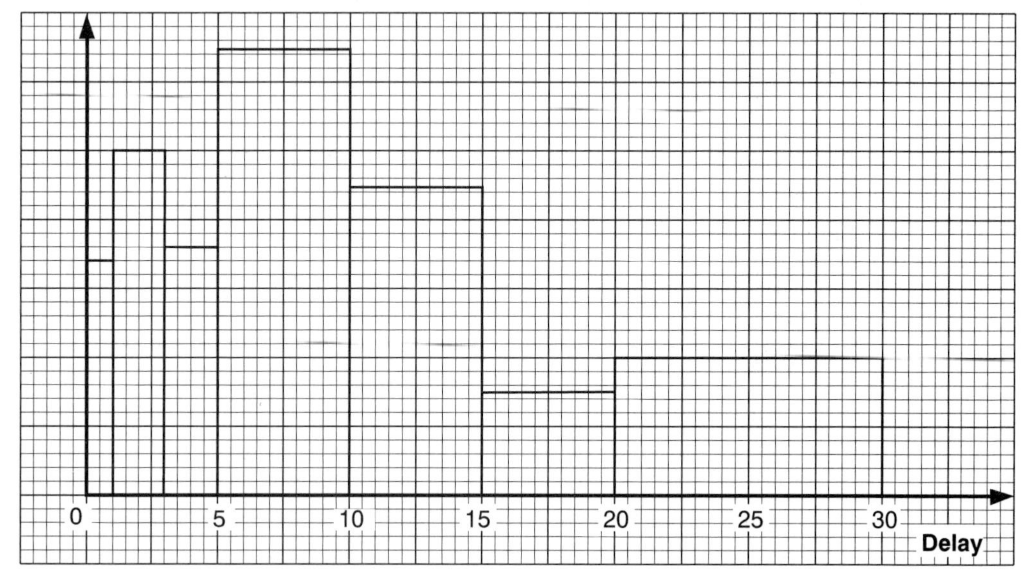

(a) Criticise the construction and presentation of this illustration.

(b) Draw your own histogram to represent these data and state any different impressions it displays from those in the illustration above.

The report also stated that, when an appointment is delayed, the median delay is 6.0 minutes, but that 50% of all appointments experience delays of less than 4.7 minutes.

(c) Show, by appropriate calculation, why **both** these statements are correct.

[AEB 1991]

8 The following table is extracted from a census report. It shows the age distribution of the population present on census night in Copeland, an area of Cumbria.

Population aged					
0–4	5–15	16–24	25–44	45–74	75 & over
4462	12 214	10 898	19 309	22 820	3364

Illustrate the data by means of a histogram. Make a suitable assumption about the upper bound of the class '75 and over'.

[AEB 1991]

SUMMARY

Now you have completed this section, you should appreciate that:

- a histogram is a diagram of a frequency table and can show absolute or relative (percentage) frequencies
- a frequency polygon and a frequency curve allow us to see the overall pattern of the distribution
- percentiles, deciles and quartiles divide the distribution into equal parts and are estimated from the cumulative frequency polygon
- a stem and leaf diagram is a useful way of representing discrete data
- a box and whisker plot illustrates range and clustering for both discrete and continuous data.

SECTION

3

Measures of average

INTRODUCTION In the previous section we examined a variety of methods for presenting data diagrammatically. We saw that such diagrams help us to identify the important features of a data set: patterns and trends, for example. The next stage in this descriptive process is to extract detailed statistical information from a data set in order to quantify such patterns and trends, and to describe in numerical terms the key features of some set of data.

By the end of this section you should be able to:

- calculate the mean for raw and aggregated data
- calculate the median for raw and aggregated data
- estimate the median from the ogive
- find the mode
- interpret and use the different measures of average.

The arithmetic mean

One of the first calculations we would normally require is to determine a typical, or average, value. The concept of average is one that most people are familiar with. In statistics, however, there are a variety of different measures of average and we examine the first of these: the **arithmetic mean**.

Let us return to the examples we were examining in the last section – heights of males and females.

Suppose we are told that the average height of males, based on the data collected, is 175.5 cm. What meaning can we attach to this statement?

In our example, we would probably think of the average height as a statistic which represented a typical height of an adult male. We might go on to say that we would not expect every adult male to be 175.5 cm tall, but rather that this height reflects some usual value. As we shall see we would actually want to know which measure of average the figure actually represented before interpreting the result in detail.

The **arithmetic mean** (usually just referred to as 'the mean') is probably the most common measure of average and it is defined as follows:

For the set of n items of data $\{ x_1, x_2, x_3, \dots x_n \}$

$$\bar{x} = \frac{x_1 + x_2 + x_3 + \dots + x_n}{n}$$

which, using the sigma notation from P1, abbreviates to:

$$\text{Arithmetic mean } \bar{x} = \frac{1}{n} \sum_{i=1}^{n} x_i$$

where:

$x_1, x_2, \dots$ are the values of the variate X

Σ is the summation symbol telling us to add all the items of data together

n is the symbol for the number of items in the data set, e.g. in the example below $n = 5$

$\bar{x}$ (pronounced 'x bar') is the standard symbol for the arithmetic mean of a set of sample data.

Example Find the arithmetic mean of the following heights of males (cm)

$\{ 168.3, 175.2, 195.3, 163.0, 175.0 \}$

Solution

$$\bar{x} = \frac{1}{5}(168.3 + 175.2 + 195.3 + 163.0 + 175.0)$$

$$\Rightarrow \bar{x} = \frac{1}{5} \times 876.8$$

$$\Rightarrow \bar{x} = 175.4 \text{ cm (1 d.p.)}$$

The arithmetic mean for a *frequency distribution* can best be found through a simple example.

Example Some students collect the information shown in Table 3.1 about the numbers of children in their families. Calculate the mean of these family sizes.

Table 3.1

Number of children in family (x)	*Number of families f*
1	3
2	9
3	5
4	2
5	1

Solution To calculate the mean of these family sizes, we need to add up all the family sizes and divide by the number of families surveyed.

i.e. $$\bar{x} = \frac{(1+1+1) + (2+2+2+2+2+2+2+2+2) + (3+3+3+3+3) + (4+4) + (5)}{3 + 9 + 5 + 2 + 1}$$

This can be written much more conveniently as:

$$\bar{x} = \frac{3 \times 1 + 9 \times 2 + 5 \times 3 + 2 \times 4 + 1 \times 5}{3 + 9 + 5 + 2 + 1}$$

or, symbolically, $\bar{x} = \frac{\Sigma fx}{\Sigma f} = \frac{49}{20} = 2.45$

This is often most conveniently worked out by using another column on the distribution table.

Table 3.2

Number of children in family (x)	Number of families f	fx
1	3	$1 \times 3 = 3$
2	9	$2 \times 9 = 18$
3	5	$3 \times 5 = 15$
4	2	$4 \times 2 = 8$
5	1	$5 \times 1 = 5$
	$\Sigma f = 20$	$\Sigma fx = 49$

So $\bar{x} = \frac{\Sigma fx}{\Sigma f}$ i.e. the total of the fx column divided by the total of the f column.

Or $\bar{x} = \frac{1}{n} \Sigma fx$ where n (as usual) represents the total number of items in the survey.

$$= \frac{49}{20} = 2.45$$

Interpreting and using the mean

As with every statistic it is important not just to be able to get the right answer, but also to be able to use the statistic properly. Most statistics are open to misinterpretation.

Let us return to our first example. We have seen that the mean height is 175.4 cm, which indicates what a person's height would be if everyone were the same height. Clearly, this is not likely to be the case. Indeed in our small example, only 2 out of 5 males have an actual height close to the mean. One person (at 195.3 cm) is some considerable way above the average. It is for this reason that we will usually want to look at the mean, not by itself, but together with other statistics calculated from the same set of data.

However, to illustrate the use of the mean let us return to our samples of males and females. If we perform the corresponding calculations (and you may want to do this yourself just to get practice), we find that:

$\bar{x}$ = 175.4 cm for the sample of males

$\bar{x}$ = 166.8 cm for the sample of females.

We could reasonably conclude that, on average, the mean height of males is almost 9 cm higher than that of females. This is not to say that all males are taller than females. We know, in fact, that this is not the case from the original data. We are saying that *typically* a male will be taller than a female.

The arithmetic mean for aggregated data

In the calculations above we used the raw data to calculate the mean. Where we have data in the form of a frequency table the method of calculation is slightly different. The reason for this becomes apparent if we examine Table 3.3 which shows the frequency table for male heights.

Table 3.3 Frequency table for males

Heights cm	*Number of males*
155–	1
160–	3
165–	8
170–	12
175–	14
180–	9
185–	2
190–	0
195–	1
Total frequency	50

Once we analyse a frequency table we no longer have the individual figures available which we need to sum in order to calculate the mean.

Looking at Table 3.3 we can see, for example, that there are eight males with a height somewhere between 165 and 170 cm but we do not know from the table precisely what these heights are.

To get round the problem we make a simplifying assumption – that the observations in a particular interval are evenly spread through that interval. This means that adding all their values would give the same answer as if they were all in the middle of the interval (referred to as the **mid-interval value**).

So, for this interval in the table, we assume that all eight males had a height of 167.5 cm. Similarly we can readily calculate the midpoint values for the other intervals.

To calculate the mean we take the mid-interval value, multiply this by the frequency of that interval, add these results together, and divide by the total frequency.

In mathematical terms this will give:

$$\bar{x} = \frac{\Sigma fx}{\Sigma f}$$

where f is the symbol for the frequency in an interval, x refers to the midpoint of an interval, and Σf will be the total frequency.

The relevant calculations are shown in Table 3.4.

Table 3.4 Calculation of mean for grouped data (heights of adult males)

	Number of males f	*Mid-interval value* x	*Frequency × mid-interval value* fx
155–	1	157.5	157.5
160–	3	162.5	487.5
165–	8	167.5	1340.0
170–	12	172.5	2070.0
175–	14	177.5	2485.0
180–	9	182.5	1642.5
185–	2	187.5	375.0
190–	0	192.5	0
195–	1	197.5	197.5
	Σf = 50		Σfx = 8755.0

$$\text{Mean} = \frac{\Sigma fx}{\Sigma f} = \frac{8755.0}{50} = 175.1 \text{ cm}$$

You should now be able to complete Exercise 1 on page 42.

The mean based on the aggregated data gives a slightly different value from that based on the raw data. The reason for this is as follows. We had to make a simplifying assumption about the values within each interval so that we could calculate the mean for the aggregated data. This will clearly lead to some discrepancy between the two calculations. The values produced from the aggregated data are less accurate: they are only an estimate of the true sample mean.

Two additional points should be noted about the grouped mean:

- It will be affected by the intervals, and therefore by the mid-interval value, which have been chosen. A different choice of intervals may lead to a slightly different estimate of the sample mean.
- The grouped mean will be influenced by any assumptions made about any open-ended intervals in the frequency table. Different assumptions will again lead to a different estimated value for the sample mean.

The median

Whilst the mean is a common and easily understood statistic, it may not always give a realistic picture of the values in the data set. We may wish to use a different measure of average than the mean for some sets of data. One of these is called the **median**.

Consider the data below, relating to the heights of nine adult males.

168.3 167.2 169.1 167.7 166.5 169.1 195.3 163.0 165.0 cm

The mean is calculated as 170.1 cm but it is clear that this is not really a typical height, given that eight of the nine observations fall below the mean. It is evident on reflection that this has happened because one number, 195.3, is much higher than the others.

The median is an alternative measure of average that can be useful in such situations. *The median is literally the middle value in the data set: that is a value such that there is the same number of values above the median as below.* Unlike the mean the median always splits the ordered set of data into two equal parts.

The median is calculated by first ranking the data from lowest to highest.

163.0 165.0 166.5 167.2 167.7 168.3 169.1 169.1 195.3 cm

and then locating the middle item. In this case item number 5 is the middle item as there are the same number of observations below this value as above it. In this example there are four people below the median height and four people above it. (Note that we carefully distinguish between the **median item** and the **median value**.)

The only point to note relates to the determination of the median item. In general we can determine which observation this will be by using:

$$\frac{n+1}{2}$$

where n is the total number of observations in the data set.
In our example this is:

$$\frac{9+1}{2} = \frac{10}{2} = 5$$

So the observation in the middle of the data set is item 5. We hit a snag if we have an even number of items. Suppose that the data here also included someone of height 164.0 cm. Then we have:

163.0, 164.0, 165.0, 166.5, 167.2, 167.7, 168.3, 169.1, 169.1, 195.3

Counting in from the ends, we find that we cannot identify a middle item. But we can find a *middle pair* (here 167.2 and 167.7).

The convention is that we take as median the number half-way between the two (167.45) or, if you like, the *mean* of the middle pair: $\frac{167.2 + 167.7}{2} = 167.45$.

There are two points to note:

- The median here is not a member of the original data set.
- We have here 10 items; the rule $\frac{n+1}{2}$ would give us $\frac{11}{2} = 5.5$.

  We still use that rule and take it to indicate that the middle pair is given by the items ranking either side of 5.5 – i.e. 5th and 6th – and we would determine the median value from these items.

You should now be able to complete Exercises 2–3 on page 42.

Calculating the median from aggregated data

As with the mean we may need to calculate the median from grouped data. Again, we must remember that in such a case the value we obtain will only be an estimate of the sample median value. Let us examine Table 3.5 which again shows the frequency distribution of heights of adult males.

Table 3.5

Heights cm	Number of males	Cumulative frequency
155–	1	1
160–	3	4
165–	8	12
170–	12	24
175–	14	38
180–	9	47
185–	2	49
190–	0	49
195–	1	50
Total	50	50

First we identify the median item. Here,

$$\frac{n+1}{2} = \frac{50+1}{2} = 25.5$$

As we are dealing with aggregated data we must identify the interval in which the median item falls. From the cumulative frequencies we see that the median item occurs in the interval $175 \le x < 180$ cm. We refer to this interval as the **median interval**.

We now know that the median item is one of the 14 values falling in this interval. Although there are 14 items in this interval we do not know what their exact values are. Again, as with the grouped mean, we make a simplifying assumption to enable us to perform the necessary calculations.

We assume that these 14 items are spread equally throughout the interval. Given that we have 14 items and that the interval covers 5 cm, this means that we can work out how far apart each item is from its neighbours.

$$\text{Distance apart} = \frac{\text{Interval width}}{\text{Interval frequency}} = \frac{5}{14} = 0.357 \text{ cm}$$

From Table 3.5 we know that the median item (25.5) is actually 1.5 items into the median interval (given that there were a total of 24 items up to this interval). Given that each item in this interval is 0.357 cm apart, this means that the median item is 0.536 cm into this interval (that is, 1.5×0.357). Given that the interval starts at 175 cm this implies the median value is:

$$175 + 0.536 \text{ cm} = 175.54 \text{ (to 2 d.p.)}$$

The method here is called **linear interpolation**. The assumption being made in this method is that the data in an interval is spread evenly throughout that interval.

You should now be able to answer Exercises 4–5 on page 42.

Estimating the median from the ogive

As well as calculating a value for the median of an aggregated data set, it is also possible to estimate the median value from the appropriate **cumulative frequency curve**, also known as an **ogive** (pronounced 'oh-jive'). The cumulative frequency curve is a modified version of the cumulative frequency polygon and simply involves smoothing the lines of the polygon into a curve.

Figure 3.1 shows the percentage ogive derived from the percentage frequency polygon in Figure 2.7.

Figure 3.1

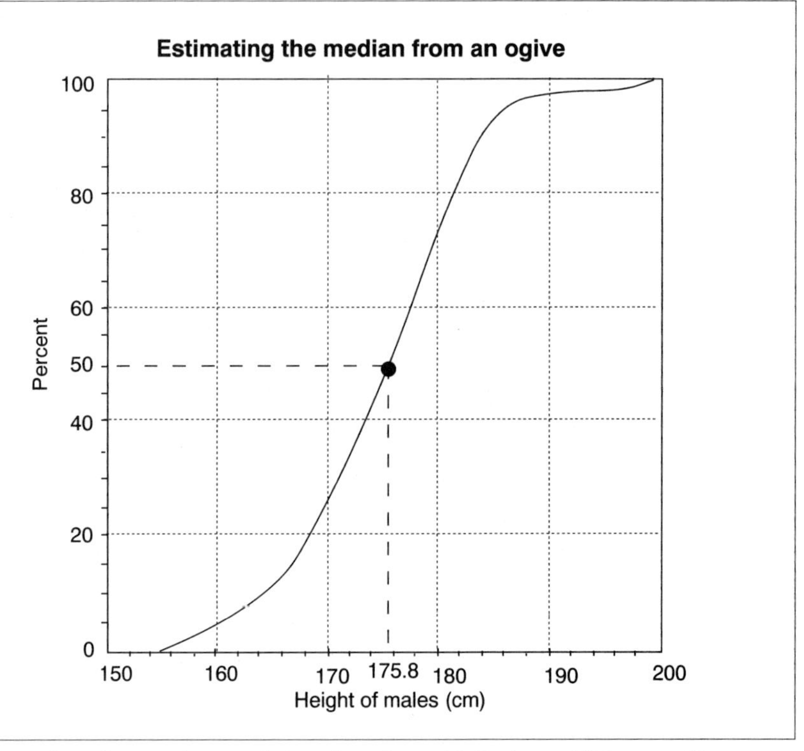

We know that the median is defined as the middle item. This actually corresponds to the middle quartile (at the 50% position on the percentage cumulative frequency axis). If we draw a line from this point to the ogive curve and down to the height axis we estimate the median to be roughly 175.8 cm.

We should remember that estimating the median from the ogive graph will be inaccurate because of the limitations of the scales on the graph.

It should also be noted that if we use the formula $\frac{n+1}{2}$ here to find which is the median item, we would get 50.5. The loss of accuracy by using 50 (the more 'obvious' choice from the diagram) is not significant and it is perfectly acceptable to use 50 as the middle value.

The mode

The third measure of average that we consider is the **mode**. The mode is defined as the value that occurs *most frequently* in a set of data. The mode is useful only when we are dealing with a discrete variable.

For example, we could determine the mode for:

- the average number of persons per family
- the average number of exam passes at a school
- the average shoe size

and so on. For example, for the average number of exam passes at a school the mode would indicate the number of exams that most pupils passed. In this sense it can be regarded as a typical value.

One of the drawbacks of the mode is that it is not always defined. A distribution may have two values sharing the highest frequency. Such a distribution is sometimes described as **bimodal** – having two modes. If there are more than two values sharing the highest frequency, it's usual to admit defeat and say that the distribution has no mode.

The modal class

For continuous data, grouped into a frequency table, although we can't find a single value as the mode, it is possible to refer to the **modal class**, i.e. the class with the highest frequency, e.g. in Table 3.3, the modal class is 175– with a frequency of 14. Of course, like its discrete counterpart, the modal class may not be uniquely defined.

Comparing the different measures of average

Considering that there are three main measures of average, we must pose the question: which measure of average do you use? The answer, as always with statistics, is that it depends.

It depends both on the data that you are analysing and what the results of the analysis will be used for.

All three statistics have their particular uses and their disadvantages, and the only real answer is to consider carefully the problem you are working on.

- *The mean* is the most commonly used statistic, often chosen because it is the only one which uses the entire data set in its calculation. Consequently it can often be used in additional calculations. The problem with the mean, as we have seen, is that it is easily distorted by relatively few extreme values.
- *The median* is less affected by extremes and provides some information about the spread of values in the data set. The difficulty with the median is that it only uses part of the data.
- *The mode* tends to be useful in fairly limited circumstances, mostly when dealing with discrete data.

Use of coding and scaling in calculating $\bar{x}$

Look at the following example.

Example Calculate the mean of the discrete data given in the following frequency table.

x	132–135	136–148	149–155	156–160
f	6	12	38	8

Solution It should be clear that the mean is around 150. The method of **coding** assumes a sensible value for $\bar{x}$ and deducts this value from all the items of data, finds the average of the resulting data and adds it on at the end.

In table form:

x	f	midpoint of interval, m	$m - 150$	$(m - 150) \times f$
132–135	6	133.5	–16.5	–99
136–148	12	141.5	–8.5	–102
149–155	38	152	2	76
156–160	8	158	8	64
	64			–61

Coded mean $= \dfrac{-61}{64} = -0.95$

Correct mean $= 150 - 0.95 = 149.05$

It is possible to use a similar technique, called **scaling**, whereby you reduce all the items of data by a factor.

Example Calculate the mean of:

6200, 5100, 7800, 9300, 8200

Example We could proceed by dividing each item by 1000, finding the mean of the resulting numbers and then multiplying by 1000 at the end.

Scaled data is $\{6.2, 5.1, 7.8, 9.3, 8.2\}$

$\bar{x}$ for scaled data is $\dfrac{36.6}{5} = 7.32$

therefore $\bar{x}$ for the original data is $7.32 \times 1000 = 7320$

You should now be able to answer Exercise 6 on page 42.

Weighted averages

Finally in this section we examine a special type of average: the weighted average, or more correctly the weighted mean.

Consider the data shown in Table 3.6.

Table 3.6

Item	*Quantity purchased*	*Price per unit £'s*
A	10	6.50
B	20	3.25
C	15	5.20

We can consider the data as showing the quantity of three similar products purchased by an individual and the price paid for each product. We may wish to calculate the average (mean) price per item.

If we work out $\frac{6.50 + 3.25 + 5.20}{3} = £4.98$ the calculation ignores the fact that different quantities of the three products are bought and so would be a fairly meaningless statistic in this case. It would ignore the fact that the individual prices have differing degrees of importance. Instead we can calculate a weighted average:

$$\text{Weighted mean} = \frac{\Sigma wx}{\Sigma w}$$

where w refers to the weights (or measures the relative importance) of the items making up the average. In this example, the weight of each item will be the number of that item purchased. The greater the number, the more important is that item.

We now calculate the weighted mean for this data:

$$\text{Weighted mean} = \frac{(10 \times 6.50) + (20 \times 3.25) + (15 \times 5.20)}{(10 + 20 + 15)}$$

$$= \frac{208}{45} = £4.62 \text{ to nearest p.}$$

That is, the weighted average price per item is £4.62. This is the average price reflecting the different quantities purchased.

You should now be able to complete Exercises 7–8 on pages 42–43.

EXERCISES

1 Calculate the mean for females based on Table 2.2 from the last section (i.e. using the frequency table you found in Exercise 2 at the end of Section 2). Why are the means based on the grouped data slightly different from those based on the raw data?

2 Find the mean of the following:

3, 8, 4, 9, 6, 8, 7, 7, 2

What is the median value?

3 Find the mean and median of the following:

4, 8, 11, 12, 6, 1

4 Find the mean of this data:

x	5	6	7	8	9	10
f	2	7	12	10	5	4

5 Estimate the mean and median of the following frequency distribution

x	0–4	4–8	8–12	12–16	16–20
f	3	8	19	14	6

6 Use sensible coding to find $\bar{x}$ for each of the following:

(a)

x	235–240	241–250	251–260	261–265
f	12	40	45	8

(b) { 42 350, 36 890, 61 350, 53 400, 48 610 }

7 If $\bar{x}$ is the mean of

$$\{ x_1, x_2, x_3, \dots x_n \}$$

find in terms of $\bar{x}$ the means of:

(a) $\{ x_1 + a, x_2 + a, x_3 + a, \dots x_n + a \}$

(b) $\{ bx_1, bx_2, bx_3, \dots bx_n \}$

8 In a shopping survey, it was decided to compare the costs of articles in two shops by means of a weighted average. The table shows the unit costs in each shop and weightings the statisticians decided to use.

	Price (p)		
	Shop A	*Shop B*	*Weighting*
White bread	39	45	5
Baked beans	25	23	2
Cornflakes	80	65	2
Cheese	140	130	3
Ice cream	125	175	1

Work out the two weighted averages and so compare the costs in the two shops.

SUMMARY

Now you have completed this section you should appreciate that:

- *averages* attempt to represent a typical value for a set of data
- *the mean* is calculated by totalling all the values in the data set and dividing this total by the number of data items in the data set
- *the median* represents the middle value in an ordered data set and always divides the data into two equal parts such that the same number of items lies above as below the median
- *the median* is to be preferred to the mean as a measure of average where the mean may be distorted by a few extreme values
- *the mode* is the most frequent value in a set of data and, for grouped data, *the modal class* is the class with the highest frequency.

SECTION

4

Dispersion

INTRODUCTION

In Section 3 we examined a number of statistical measures of average and saw that such averages do not always reflect a 'typical' value in the data set. The individual items in a data set may vary considerably from the average. We need to introduce further statistics which allow us to describe and quantify such variation, or dispersion as it is known in statistics.

By the end of this section you should be able to understand and interpret:

- the range
- the standard deviation
- the variance
- the interquartile range
- skewness.

The range

The range is the simplest measure of dispersion. For a set of data it is defined as follows

Range = largest item – smallest item

It is very easily calculated but tells us nothing about the *distribution* of data within the set of data. For the data sets in Section 2, pp. 8–9, the ranges are:

Range of male heights = 195.3 – 159.8 = 35.5 cm

Range of female heights = 181.9 – 153.3 = 28.6 cm

This suggests that male heights are more variable than female heights. In some circumstances the range can give a rough and ready measure of the 'spreadout-ness' of data but would not be of such use where data is very skewed (see page 54).

The standard deviation

The standard deviation is the measure of variation most often used in statistics: it measures variation around the arithmetic mean.

Standard deviation is defined by the following formula:

$$\text{Standard deviation} \quad s = \sqrt{\frac{\sum_{i=1}^{n}(x_i - \bar{x})^2}{n}}$$

where the set of data is: $\{x_1, x_2, x_3 \ldots x_n\}$ (i.e. n items of data)

From the formula above, if we square both sides we get:

$$\text{Variance } s^2 = \frac{\Sigma(x_i - \bar{x})^2}{n}$$

This quantity is called the **variance** of the data. In later work, the variance will turn out to be used more often than the standard deviation as a measure of disperson.

An example showing how to calculate *s* and how to set out the calculation now follows.

Example Calculate the standard deviation of the set of data { 4, 5, 7, 9, 10 }.

Solution The calculations are set out in Table 4.1 which is followed by an explanation.

Table 4.1 Calculation of standard deviation

x_i	$x_i - \bar{x}$	$(x_i - \bar{x})^2$
4	4 − 7 = − 3	9
5	5 − 7 = − 2	4
7	7 − 7 = 0	0
9	9 − 7 = 2	4
10	10 − 7 = 3	9
$\Sigma x_i = 35$		$\Sigma(x_i - \bar{x})^2 = 24$

$$\Rightarrow \bar{x} = \frac{35}{5} = 7 \qquad \Rightarrow s^2 = \frac{24}{5} = 4.8$$

$$\Rightarrow s = 2.19$$

In the first column are the individual items of data. (With grouped data, this column would contain the mid-interval values – see the example on page 48.) The first column is totalled and the result divided by 5 to give $\bar{x}$, the mean. This is then used in the second column to calculate the deviation of each item of data from the mean.

If these deviations are totalled, the result will always be zero (or thereabouts, if rounding has been necessary), i.e. the positive deviations cancel the negative deviations. For this reason it is necessary to square the deviations and this is done in column 3.

Column 3 is totalled and then, beneath the table, the final calculation of s is carried out. The total is divided by 5, the number of items of data (this is averaging the squared deviations) and the result of this is then square-rooted (to offset the original effect of squaring).

This method of calculating the standard deviation looks straightforward enough with the easy numbers in this example. But, if the mean is not a whole number, subtracting it from every value and then squaring the result involves a lot of decimal places and/or a lot of rounding. There is an easier method!

The calculating formula

Deriving the formula for the easier method looks anything but easy, but using the resulting formula does save a very great deal of work.

Consider $\Sigma(x_i - \bar{x})^2$, then writing out the terms gives

$$\sum_{i=1}^{n} (x_i - \bar{x})^2 = (x_1 - \bar{x})^2 + (x_2 - \bar{x})^2 + (x_3 - \bar{x})^2 + \ldots + (x_n - \bar{x})^2$$

$$= (x_1^2 - 2x_1\bar{x} + \bar{x}^2) + (x_2^2 - 2x_2\bar{x} + \bar{x}^2)$$

$$+ \ldots + \ldots + (x_n^2 - 2x_n\bar{x} + \bar{x}^2) \quad \text{(by multiplying out the brackets)}$$

$$= (x_1^2 + x_2^2 + \ldots x_n^2) + (\bar{x}^2 + \bar{x}^2 + \ldots + \bar{x}^2)$$

$$- (2x_1\bar{x} + 2x_2\bar{x} + \ldots 2x_n\bar{x})$$

$$= \sum_{i=1}^{n} x_i^2 + n\bar{x}^2 - 2\bar{x}(x_1 + x_2 + \ldots + x_n)$$

$$= \sum_{i=1}^{n} x_i^2 + n\bar{x}^2 - 2\bar{x} \times n\bar{x} \quad \left(\text{using the fact that } \frac{x_1 + x_2 + \ldots + x_n}{n} = \bar{x}\right)$$

$$= \sum_{i=1}^{n} x_i^2 + n\bar{x}^2 - 2n\bar{x}^2$$

$$= \sum_{i=1}^{n} x_i^2 - n\bar{x}^2$$

Now using the formula for variance: $s^2 = \dfrac{\sum_{i=1}^{n}(x_i - \bar{x})^2}{n}$

this now becomes: $s^2 = \dfrac{\sum_{i=1}^{n} x_i^2 - n\bar{x}^2}{n}$ $\Rightarrow$

$$s^2 = \frac{\sum_{i=1}^{n} x_i^2}{n} - \bar{x}^2$$

which in practice is a much simpler formula to use. You shouldn't be too concerned if you find the method difficult to follow here. The result is important though.

Calculation of standard deviation and variance is made very much simpler by using this version of the formula.

Example Calculate s for this set of data, first using the definition of s and then using the calculating formula:

{168.3, 175.2, 195.3, 163.0, 175.0}

Solution The calculations are as follows.

Table 4.2 **Calculation of standard deviation**

x_i	$x_i - \bar{x}$	$(x_i - \bar{x})^2$	x_i^2
168.3	−7.06	49.84	28 324.89
175.2	−0.16	0.03	30 695.04
195.3	+19.94	397.60	38 142.09
163.0	−12.36	152.77	26 569.00
175.0	−0.36	0.13	30 625.00
$\Sigma x_i = 876.8$		$\Sigma(x_i - \bar{x})^2 = 600.37$	$\Sigma(x_i^2) = 154\,356.02$

Both methods use the first column to find $\bar{x}$ in the same way:

$$\bar{x} = \frac{876.8}{5} = 175.36$$

The first method, using the definition of s, then uses this value of $\bar{x}$ to work out the values of $(x_i - \bar{x})$ and $(x_i - \bar{x})^2$ in columns 2 and 3.

Then the total of column 3 has to be divided by the number of items:

$$s^2 = \frac{600.37}{5} = 120.074$$

$$\Rightarrow s = 10.96$$

The second method, using the calculating formula, doesn't need columns 2 and 3 – just column 4 (which is much more straightforward to work out).

It then continues:

$$s^2 = \frac{154\,356.02}{5} - 175.36^2 = 120.074 \Rightarrow s = 10.96$$

In a problem with more values in it than in this one, the saving of effort over the first method is very welcome. It should be your usual way to work out a standard deviation.

Calculating the standard deviation for aggregated data

We have seen in earlier sections that we need to be able to calculate appropriate statistics, not only from a set of raw data, but also directly from a frequency table. The same applies to the standard deviation.

Example

Let us return once more to the frequency table for the heights of adult males where we have already calculated the mean (from the frequency table) as 175.1 cm. The method we adopt is similar in approach to that of calculating the mean from a frequency table: we use midpoint values to estimate the individual data items.

Just as we had a formula for calculating the standard deviation for raw data so we have a formula for the aggregated data:

$$\text{Standard deviation} = \sqrt{\frac{\Sigma fx^2}{\Sigma f} - \left(\frac{\Sigma fx}{\Sigma f}\right)^2} = s$$

Table 4.3 shows the various calculations that we need to undertake to work out the standard deviation from the frequency table.

Table 4.3 Calculation of the standard deviation for grouped data (heights of males)

Interval (cm)	*Frequency f*	*Midpoint x*	*fx*	*fx*^{2} *
155–	1	157.5	157.5	24,806.25
160–	3	162.5	487.5	79,218.75
165–	8	167.5	1340.0	224,450.00
170–	12	172.5	2070.0	357,075.00
175–	14	177.5	2485.0	441,087.50
180–	9	182.5	1642.5	299,756.25
185–	2	187.5	375.0	70,312.50
190–	0	192.5	0	0
195–	1	197.5	197.5	39,006.25
Total	50		8755.0	1,535,712.50

*You can calculate fx^2 as $x \times fx$.

We are now in a position to put all the appropriate values into the formula and to work out the answer.

For the adult males:

$$\text{Standard deviation} = \sqrt{\frac{\Sigma fx^2}{\Sigma f} - \left(\frac{\Sigma fx}{\Sigma f}\right)^2} = \sqrt{\frac{1{,}535{,}712.5}{50} - \left(\frac{8755}{50}\right)^2}$$

$$= \sqrt{30{,}714.25 - 30{,}660.01}$$

$$= \sqrt{54.24} = 7.36 \text{ cm} = s$$

That is, the standard deviation of heights of adult males is 7.36 cm. It is often difficult to assess the use of a single standard deviation, but this figure, particularly when compared with the mean value, tends to suggest relatively low dispersion. That is, most, but not all, of the data is clustered around the mean value.

You should now be able to answer Exercises 1–3 on page 56.

As with the mean and median we should see the calculation of the standard deviation for grouped data as an estimate of the value which would be obtained directly from the raw data. Manual calculation of the standard deviation for the raw data, however, is extremely time-consuming and tedious for anything more than a few numbers and the calculation based on the grouped data is usually used.

Some problems involve combining two sets of data and finding means and variances.

Example

(a) The lengths of 20 rods are measured in cm

The measurements are summarised by $\sum x = 285$, $\sum x^2 = 4250$. Calculate $\bar{x}$ and s^2.

(b) The sample is enlarged by a further 10 rods.

The lengths of these 10 rods may be summarised by $\sum x = 155$, $\sum x^2 = 2300$. Calculate the mean and variance of the whole sample of 30 rods.

Solution

(a) $\bar{x} = \dfrac{285}{20} = 14.25$ cm

$$s^2 = \frac{\sum x^2}{n} - \bar{x}^2 = \frac{4250}{20} - 14.25^2 = 9.4375 \text{ cm}$$

(b) $\sum x$ for the 30 rods is found by adding the $\sum x$ figures for both parts of the sample. $\sum x = 285 + 155 = 440$

$$\Rightarrow \bar{x} = \frac{440}{30} = 14.67 \text{ (2 d.p.)}$$

Similarly, adding the two sets of $\sum x^2$ figures:

$\sum x^2 = 4250 + 2300 = 6550$

$$\Rightarrow s^2 = \frac{6550}{30} - 14.67^2 = 3.22.$$

You should now be able to answer Exercise 4 on page 56.

Using your calculator to find mean and standard deviation

It is instructive to be able to calculate the mean and standard deviation long-hand but, in practice, you let your calculator do the work for you. The procedure is as follows:

1 Put the standard deviation mode on.
(This is usually indicated by SD.)

2 Clear the memory.
(Usually this is either [inv] [AC] or [Shift] [AC].)

3 Feed in your figures.

(If the sample is *small* this usually requires either [x] [M+]

or [x] [RUN].

If the sample is *large* this usually requires [x] [×] [f] [M+]

or [x] [×] [f] [RUN].)

4 Key out the values of n (useful for a check), $\overline{x}$ and s.

(Usually this involves either:

[inv] [ ] (n), [inv] [ ] ($\overline{x}$) and [inv] [ ] (s_n) respectively or

[K out] [ ] (n), [shift] [1] ($\overline{x}$) and [shift] [2] (s_n) respectively.)

It is very important that you can use your calculator properly, so a set of examples on which you can practise now follows.

Examples on mean, variance and standard deviation

Work through the following and check that you agree with the given answers.

1 3, 4, 5, 6, 7, 8, 9

Ans: $n = 7, \overline{x} = 6, s = 2$, Variance = 4

Remember that variance = s^2 ∴ In this case variance = $2^2 = 4$.

2 4, 5, 8, 3, 7, 6, 6, 7, 1, 4

Ans: $n = 10, \ \overline{x} = 5.1, \ s = 2.022$ ∴ Variance = 4.09

3 1, 0, 2, 0, 3, 3, 0, 0, 1, 4

Ans: $n = 10, \ \overline{x} = 1.4, \ s = 1.428$ ∴ Variance = 2.04

Remember to feed in the zeros as well.

4

x	2	4	6	8	10
f	3	5	11	4	2

Ans: $n = 25, \overline{x} = 5.76, \ s = 2.141$ ∴ Variance = 4.58 (to 2 d.p.)

You begin by feeding in either:

[2] [×] [3] [M+] or [2] [×] [3] [RUN]

You must *not* begin by feeding in:

6 M+ or 6 RUN

5

x	3	6	9	12	15
f	8	11	17	9	5

Ans: $n = 50$, $\overline{x} = 8.52$, $s = 3.570$, Variance = 12.73 (to 2 d.p.)

6

x	1	3	5	7	9	11	13
f	2	5	17	21	13	0	2

Ans: $n = 60$, $\overline{x} = 6.53$ (to 2 d.p.), $s = 2.349$, Variance = 5.52 (to 2 d.p.)

7

x	0	1	2	3	4	5	6
f	8	11	27	36	21	13	4

Ans: $n = 120$, $\overline{x} = 2.88$ (to 2 d.p.), $s = 1.444$, Variance = 2.09 (to 2 d.p.)

8 Use your calculator to check the mean and standard deviation for males, as given in Table 4.3.

The safest method is to work out standard deviations using a table and then check your work using the SD mode on your calculator. It's very reassuring when two different methods agree. If they don't agree, your calculator can give you Σx and Σx^2 which may well help you to find where the mistake is.

The interquartile range

So far in looking at dispersion we have concentrated on measuring dispersion around the mean. We shall now examine how dispersion around the median can be quantified using a statistic known as the **interquartile range.**

The interquartile range is defined as:

$$\text{Interquartile range} = Q_3 - Q_1$$

where Q_3 represents the upper (75%) quartile

and Q_1 represents the lower (25%) quartile

(Recall that the upper quartile is the value in the data set which gives 25% of the data above this value and 75% below. Similarly, the lower quartile is the value in the data set which gives 25% of the data below and 75% above. Recall too that the median is the middle (50%) or second quartile.)

The upper and lower quartiles can be calculated in any one of four ways:

Method 1: From the raw data we can use the same method that we used for the median. Instead of counting along the ordered data looking for the item in the middle (the 50% item) we would look instead for the 25% item for the lower quartile and 75% item for the upper quartile.

Method 2: From the frequency table we can use a formula similar to the one we used for the median. You will remember the formula we used to determine the median item was:

$$\text{median item} = \frac{(n + 1)}{2}$$

For the lower quartile we would want item $\frac{(n+1)}{4}$ instead (because we now want the item which is $\frac{1}{4}$ of the ordered data set).

For the upper quartile we require item $\frac{3(n+1)}{4}$ because we now seek the item which is $\frac{3}{4}$ of the ordered data set.

Method 3: From the percentage ogive; again, instead of finding the median at the 50% point we would find the lower quartile at the 25% point and the upper quartile from the 75% point.

Method 4: Use of linear interpolation as explained on page 37, where for grouped data we assume that the data is evenly spread through that interval.

Which method we use will depend on the problem we are looking at and the form of any analysis and calculations that we have already undertaken.

Table 4.4 shows the quartiles for males based on Table 2.5 in Section 2, using Method 2.

Table 4.4 Quartiles for males (all figures in cm)

	Males
Lower quartile (Q_1)	170.3
Median (Q_2)	175.5
Upper quartile (Q_3)	180.1
Interquartile range ($Q_3 - Q_1$)	9.8

The table shows three quartiles (remember that the median is effectively the middle quartile) as well as the interquartile range.

The corresponding results for female heights are in Table 4.5.

Table 4.5 Quartiles for females (all figures in cm)

	Females
Lower quartile (Q_1)	161.9
Median (Q_2)	167.5
Upper quartile (Q_3)	172.1
Interquartile range ($Q_3 - Q_1$)	10.2

Let us look and see what the interquartile range can tell us about the data.

The interquartile range is the difference between the upper and lower quartile. It represents the central 50% of the distribution, that is half of the data set falls into the interquartile range. So, as a measure of dispersion the interquartile range always contains the same proportion of the data set, the middle 50% around the median.

For males the interquartile range is 9.8, whilst for females it is 10.2. The fact that the interquartile range is smaller in males indicates that the items in the middle of the data set are relatively closely clustered around the median. There is less of a difference between the top 25% height figure and the bottom 25% height figure than in females.

Skewness

We have seen over the past few sections how we can use the statistics we have introduced to describe features of the data set. One feature that we often require relates to the general shape of the distribution.

In the examples we have used in earlier sections, the shape of the distribution of the data can vary considerably.

As we have seen, the mean and median for a data set are often different. The difference will be largely due to extreme values at one end of the distribution. Suppose we had a few extremely high values in the data set. When working out the mean these numbers will be included in the calculation (remember that the mean uses all the data). These extremely high values, however, will not be included in the calculation for the median because in its calculation we only count along to the middle of the data.

So, a few extremely high values will tend to pull the mean higher than the median. Extremely low values, on the other hand, will pull the mean below the median. We can imagine encountering three general types of distribution which are illustrated in the three parts of Figure 4.1.

Figure 4.1

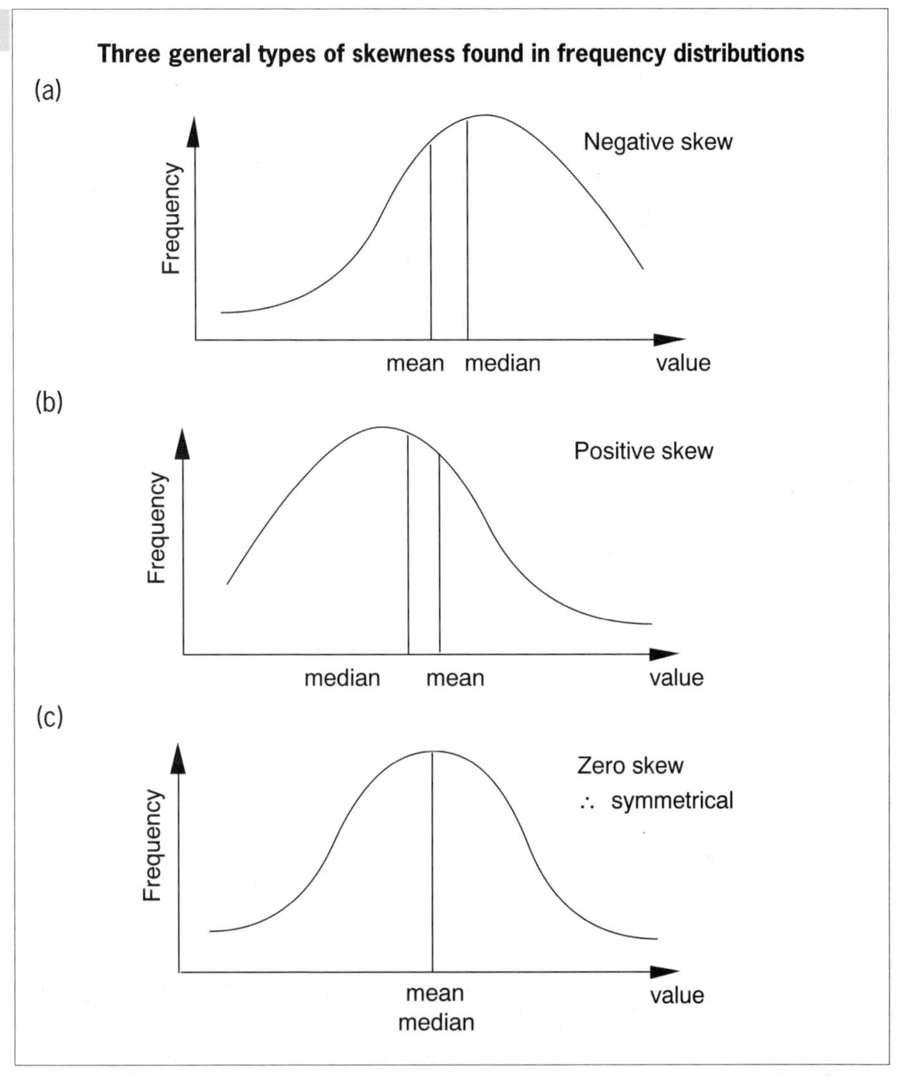

Diagram (a) illustrates a relatively small number of low values pulling the mean below the median. The mean will take a lower value than the median and we refer to this type of distribution as having a **negative skew**. The more extreme the lower values, the more the distribution will concentrate on the left-hand side and the larger the negative skewness will become.

The second diagram has a relatively small number of extremely high values, which will pull the mean above the median, giving a **positive skew**. The distribution in such a case will be concentrated on the left-hand side.

A symmetrical distribution, as in diagram (c), will have a zero skew, with the mean and median equal (or at least approximately so).

You should now be able to complete Exercises 5–10 on pages 57–59.

EXERCISES

1 Calculate the standard deviation of these data sets:

(i) using the definition of standard deviation

(ii) using the calculating formula

(a) $\{2, 7, 12, 13, 21\}$

(b)

x	4	5	6	7	8
f	3	8	12	10	2

2 Calculate the standard deviation for the heights of females using the frequency data produced in Exercise 1, Section 2.

3 Calculate the mean and variance of the data in this frequency distribution:

x	5–	10–	15–	20–	25–	30–
f	4	9	15	13	7	3

4 The weights (in kilograms) of two groups of students are measured and summarised:

	n	Σx	Σx^2
Group A	10	550	32 500
Group B	15	970	63 500

(a) Calculate the mean and variance of each group's weights.

(b) The two groups are now to be considered as a single sample of 25 students. Calculate its mean and variance.

5 Give **one** advantage and **one** disadvantage of grouping data into a frequency table.

The table shows the trunk diameters, in centimetres, of a random sample of 200 larch trees.

Diameter (cm)	15–	20–	25–	30–	35–	40–50
Frequency	22	42	70	38	16	12

Plot a cumulative frequency curve of these data.

By use of this curve, or otherwise, estimate the median and the interquartile range of the trunk diameters of larch trees.

A random sample of 200 spruce trees yields the following information concerning their trunk diameters, in centimetres.

Minimum	*Lower quartile*	*Median*	*Upper quartile*	*Maximum*
13	27	32	35	42

Use this data summary to draw a second cumulative frequency curve on your graph.

Comment on any similarities or differences between the trunk diameters of larch and spruce trees.

[AEB 1993]

6 In an investigation of delays at a roadworks, the times spent, by a sample of commuters, waiting to pass through the roadworks were recorded to the nearest minute. Shown below is part of a cumulative frequency table resulting from the investigation.

Upper class boundary	2.5	4.5	7.5	8.5	9.5	10.5	12.5	15.5	20.5
Cumulative number of commuters	0	6	21	48	97	149	178	191	200

(a) For how many of the commuters was the time recorded as 11 minutes or 12 minutes?

(b) Estimate:

(i) the lower quartile,

(ii) the 81st percentile, of these waiting times.

7 A railway enthusiast simulates train journeys and records the number of minutes, x, to the nearest minute, trains are late according to the schedule being used. A random sample of 50 journeys gave the following times.

17	5	3	10	4	3	10	5	2	14
3	14	5	5	21	9	22	36	14	34
22	4	23	6	8	15	41	23	13	7
6	13	33	8	5	34	26	17	8	43
24	14	23	4	19	5	23	13	12	10

(a) Construct a stem and leaf diagram to represent these data.

(b) Comment on the shape of the distribution produced by your diagram.

(c) Given that $\sum x = 738$ and $\sum x^2 = 16\,526$, calculate (to 2 decimal places) estimates of the mean and the variance of the population from which this sample was drawn.

(d) Explain briefly the effect that grouping of these data would have had on your calculations in (c).

8 (a) Explain how the median and quartiles of a distribution can be used when describing the shape of a distribution.

Summarised below is the distribution of masses of new potatoes, in grams to the nearest gram.

Mass (g)	*Frequency*
19 or less	2
20–29	14
30–39	21
40–44	34
45–49	39
50–59	42
60–69	13
70–79	9
80–89	4
90 or more	2

(b) Use interpolation to estimate the median and quartiles of this distribution. Hence describe its skewness.

(c) Draw a box and whisker plot to illustrate these data.

9

x	0–4	4–8	8–12	12–20
f	5	11	36	8

(a) Illustrate the above distribution with a histogram. What is the modal class?

(b) Draw a cumulative frequency polygon and hence estimate

(i) the median and (ii) the semi-interquartile range.

(c) Use your calculator to estimate the mean and standard deviation of x.

10 Estimate the interquartile range from the following data.

x	2–4	5–7	8–10	11–13
f	3	7	12	2

SUMMARY

Over the last two sections we have introduced a variety of statistics which can be used to describe the main features of a set of data.

Now you have completed this section you should appreciate that:

- the standard deviation is a statistic which measures dispersion around the arithmetic mean
- the interquartile range is the difference between the upper and lower quartile
- skewness is a measure of how symmetrical the distribution is
- other things being equal, the larger the dispersion statistic then the less typical of the data the average value becomes.
- variance = (standard deviation)^2.

And you should be able to use your calculator to quickly find the mean and standard deviation.

SECTION

5

Probability

INTRODUCTION

Whether we are explicitly aware of the fact or not, chance and uncertainty play an important part in our lives. When preparing for an exam we weigh up the chances of a particular topic appearing on the paper. When going to school or college to work each day we assess the chance that it might rain and we will need an umbrella. Such decisions have to be taken under conditions of uncertainty and it is frequently necessary to assess the likelihood of specific events occurring in the future. The analysis and quantifying of such assessments is known as probability theory, and forms the basis for important topics in statistics.

By the end of this section you should be able to:

- understand and be able to use the rules for calculating probabilities
- understand the meaning of trial, sample space and event in the context of probability
- be able to use permutations and combinations in simple cases
- understand the ideas of conditional probability and independence of events.

Trials, sample space and event

To illustrate the rules and language of probability we will consider some simple examples. An example which will be used throughout this section is as follows:

> Eight cards numbered 1, 2, 3, … , 8 but otherwise identical are placed in a container from which they can be selected randomly. In this way each card is *equally likely* to be selected.

A **trial** in probability theory is an action with several possible outcomes and for the set of 8 cards above a simple trial would be to select a single card from the container and observe the number written on it.

The set of possible outcomes for a trial is called the **sample space** (sometimes also the **possibility space**) and in this particular example it would be the set S given by:

$$S = \{1,\ 2,\ 3,\ 4,\ 5,\ 6,\ 7,\ 8\}$$

Note that provided the selection is made randomly, each of the elements of this set is equally likely to occur. A sample space could therefore be defined as 'the set of possible outcomes of a trial'.

Any subset of a sample space is called an *event*

e.g. $\{2, 4, 6, 8\}$, $\varnothing$ (the empty set)

and S are all subsets of the set S above, and are therefore events according to the definition.

(A summary of results and notation concerning sets is given in Appendix 1 at the end of the book for students who have not met them before.)

With our example of 8 numbered cards it is possible to devise more complicated trials which in turn will give rise to more complicated sample spaces and events.

Example

A card is selected, its number noted and then replaced. A second card is then selected and its number noted.

Describe the sample space and give an event associated with this sample space.

Solution

The sample space will consist of all ordered pairs of numbers (x, y) where they are both integers from 1 to 8 or more concisely

$$S = \{(x, y): \ 1 \le x \le 8, \ 1 \le y \le 8, \ x, y \text{ integers}\}$$

An example of an event associated with this S is 'the first number selected is less than the second number selected' which could be described more formally by

$$A = \{(x, y): \ 1 \le x \le 8, \ 1 \le y \le 8, \ x, y \text{ integers}, \ x < y\}$$

Events and probabilities

Returning to the sample space $S = \{1, 2, \dots 8\}$ for the single selection of a card, some events we could describe are:

$A = \{2, 3, 5, 7\}$	(a prime number is chosen)
$B = \{1, 2, 3\}$	(a card less than 4 is selected)
$\varnothing$	(no card is selected)
S	(a card is selected)

and where for example event A would be said to have occurred if one of the numbers 2, 3, 5 or 7 had been selected.

If a sample space S consists of equally likely outcomes,

then the probability of an event X is simply defined by the rule:

$$P(X) = \frac{n(X)}{n(S)}$$

and for the events above:

$$P(A) = \frac{n(\{2, 3, 5, 7\})}{n(\{1, 2, 3, \dots 8\})} = \frac{4}{8} = \frac{1}{2}$$

$$P(B) = \frac{n(\{1, 2, 3\})}{n(\{1, 2, 3, \dots 8\})} = \frac{3}{8}$$

$$P(\varnothing) = \frac{n(\varnothing)}{n(S)} = \frac{0}{8} = 0$$

$$P(S) = \frac{n(S)}{n(S)} = 1$$

It should be clear from the above that for any event X

$$0 \leq P(X) \leq 1$$

An event with probability 0 is called *impossible* and an event with probability 1 is called *certain*. All other events will have a probability ranging from unlikely, through even chance, to likely, along a scale from 0 to 1 (see Figure 5.1).

Figure 5.1

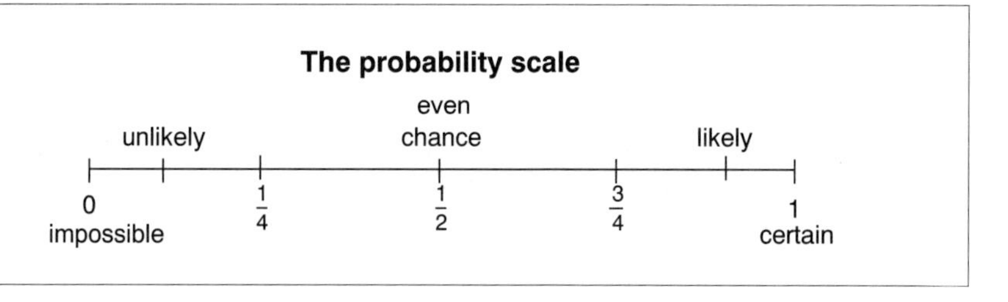

Example

From the eight numbered cards, two cards are taken one after the other and where the first is replaced before the second is taken (this method of selection is called **sampling with replacement**). The numbers on the cards chosen are added together. Find the probability of obtaining a total score between 6 and 13.

Solution

A sample space of ordered pairs can be usefully represented as a set of points on a coordinate grid as in Figure 5.2.

Figure 5.2

Showing the sample space for sampling with replacement

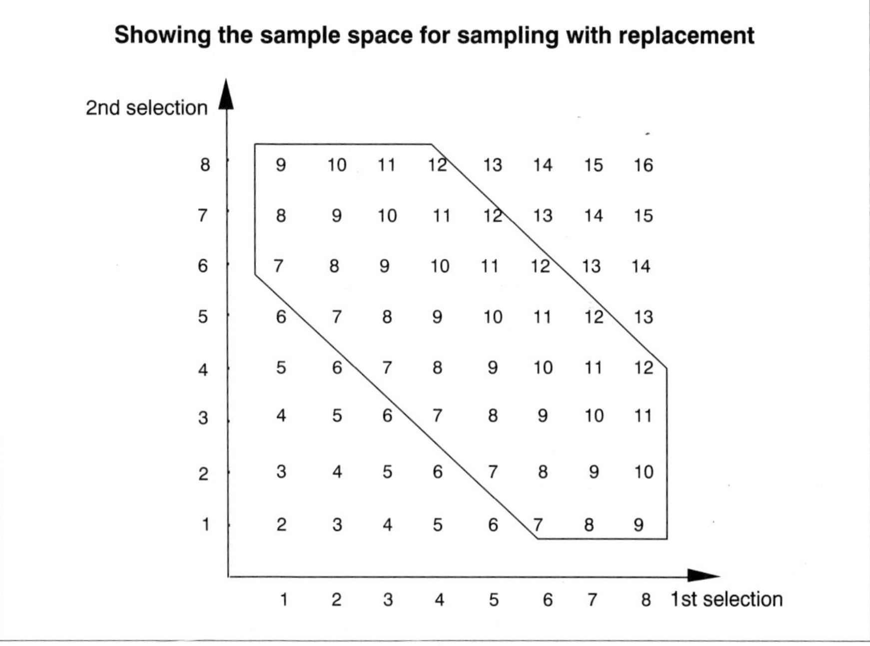

The ordered pairs which give a total satisfying 6 < score < 13 are shown enclosed in the diagram and it can now be seen that:

$$P(6 < \text{score} < 13) = \frac{39}{64}$$

Compound events

Events can be combined using the same rules and notation as for sets, to form compound events.

Example

Let $S = \{1, 2, 3, \dots, 8\}$

and $A = \{1, 3, 5, 7\}$

$B = \{1, 2, 3\}$

$C = \{7, 8\}$

Write down the events $A \cap B$, $A \cup C$, $B \cap C$, A', C', $A \cup C'$, $(A \cup C)'$ and find $P(A)$, $P(B)$, $P(C')$ $P(B \cap C)$, $P(A \cup B)$, $P(A \cap B)$.

Calculate $P(A) + P(B) - P(A \cap B)$.

Solution

$A \cap B$ = elements in common to A and B
= { 1, 3 }
$A \cup C$ = elements in A or B or both
= { 1, 3, 5, 7, 8 }
$B \cap C = \varnothing$
A' = elements which are in S but not in A
= { 2, 4, 6, 8 }
called the *complement of A*
C' = { 1, 2, 3, 4, 5, 6 }
$A \cup C'$ = { 1, 3, 5, 7 } $\cup$ { 1, 2, 3, 4, 5, 6 }
= { 1, 2, 3, 4, 5, 6, 7 }
$(A \cup C)'$ = ({ 1, 3, 5, 7 } $\cup$ { 7, 8, })'
= ({ 1, 3, 5, 7, 8 })'
= { 2, 4, 6 }
(Note how brackets make a difference here, as elsewhere in algebra.)

$$P(A) = \frac{4}{8} = \frac{1}{2}$$
$$P(B) = \frac{3}{8}$$
$$P(C') = \frac{6}{8} = \frac{3}{4}$$
$$P(B \cap C) = \frac{0}{8} = 0$$
$$P(A \cup B) = \frac{n(\{1, 3, 5, 7, 8\})}{n(S)} = \frac{5}{8}$$
$$P(A \cap B) = \frac{2}{8} = \frac{1}{4}$$

$P(A) + P(B) - P(A \cap B) = \frac{1}{2} + \frac{3}{8} - \frac{1}{4} = \frac{5}{8}$, which is the same as $P(A \cup B)$

Some important rules are suggested by this example.

Rule 1

For any event X from sample space S

$$P(X') = 1 - P(X)$$

Rule 2

For any events X and Y from a sample space S

$$P(X \cup Y) = P(X) + P(Y) - P(X \cap Y)$$

The truth of Rule 1 is illustrated in Figure 5.3.

Figure 5.3

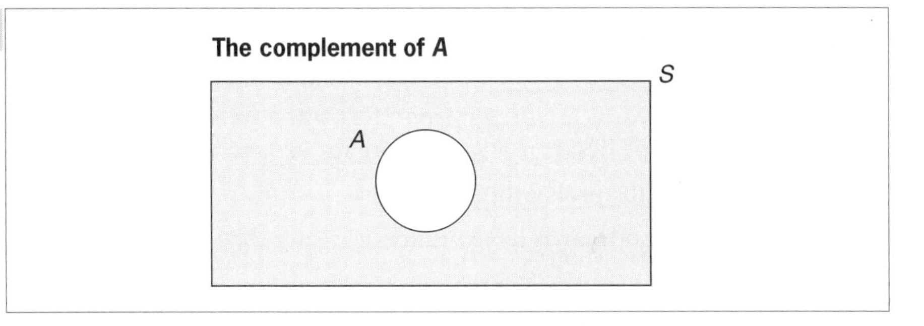

The truth of Rule 2 is more difficult to illustrate, but consider Figure 5.4.

Figure 5.4

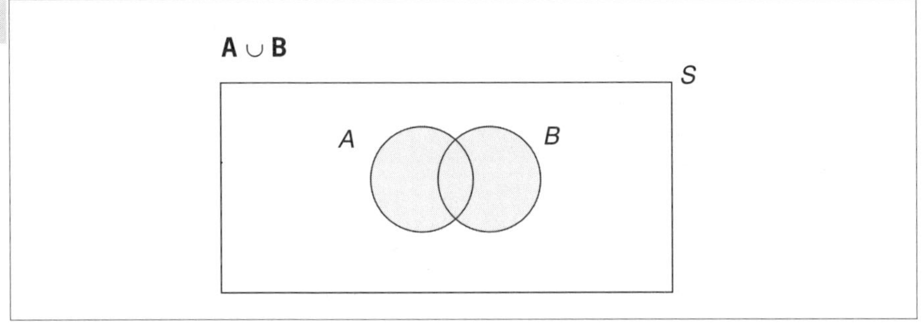

To evaluate P($A \cup B$) we could add up the probability in A and the probability in B. However in doing this, we would have added the intersection twice, so it therefore needs to be subtracted once.

In the previous Example we saw that $B \cap C = \varnothing$, and it followed that P($B \cap C$) = 0. Events which have this property are called *mutually exclusive.* Mutually exclusive events have the property that if one of them occurs then the other cannot possible occur. As an example, if you choose a card from an ordinary pack of playing cards, the events A = 'picking a black card' and B = 'picking a red card' are mutually exclusive.

You should now be able to answer Exercises 1–2 on page 79.

Some useful methods

The methods to be investigated here are best illustrated by some worked examples.

Using tree diagrams

Tree diagrams are useful in situations where there is a sequence of trials although their use becomes unwieldy if the sequence is very long or there are more than a few options at each trial. However the method is useful and illustrates several important ideas.

Example Two cards are drawn from the eight numbered cards with replacement (i.e. the first is replaced before the second is drawn).

Find the probability that:

(a) both cards have numbers greater than 5

(b) at least one of the numbers is a 6.

Solution (a) We are only concerned here with the card being > 5 or ≤ 5, so there are essentially two options at each trial.

The tree diagram (the visual aid to solving the problem) is as follows:

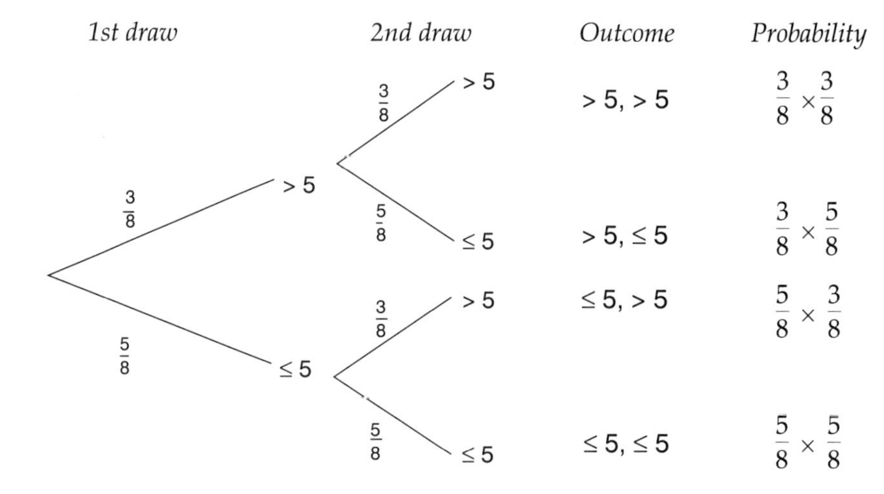

The complete tree diagram shows the outcomes at the ends of the branches and their probabilities on the branches. So at the first trial the outcome is > 5 (i.e. 6, 7 or 8) with probability $\frac{3}{8}$ as shown. After the first trial has taken place, the second card is replaced and so the probabilities at the second trial are going to be the same.

However, this time we have a second trial for each of the possible outcomes of the first trial – i.e. each branch now branches into two. The various outcomes and their probabilities are then listed at the ends of the final branches as shown.

The final column illustrates an important point which pervades probability theory.

If we consider the outcome '> 5, > 5' this is a shorthand for '> 5 and > 5' and in the final column 'and' has been replaced by '×'.

Whenever 'and' occurs in probability problems, it will be necessary to multiply the probabilities together.

We will return to this point later when the idea of independence is met but for the moment the following rule will be sufficient.

'and' $\Leftrightarrow$ $\times$

The answer to the question 'What is the probability that both cards are greater than 5?' is now seen to be $\frac{9}{64}$.

Before leaving the example it should be noted that the probabilities in the final column add up to 1 and this should always be the case for a correct tree diagram.

(b) In this part we are only concerned with whether a number is a 6 or not, so the tree diagram has the form

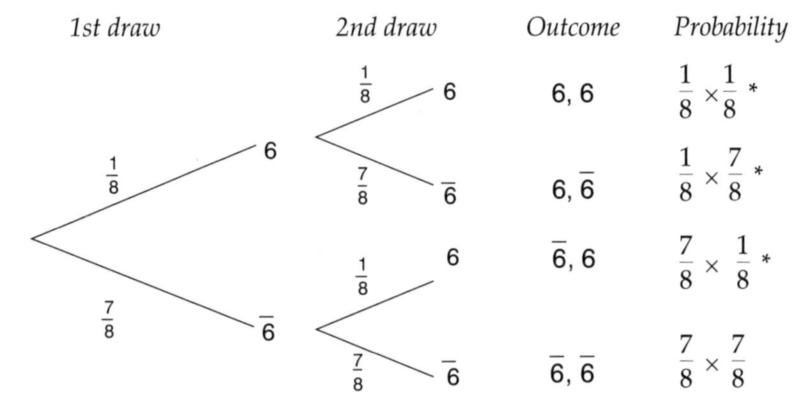

(Here $\overline{6}$ means 'not a 6' – this is another form of notation for the complement – we could also have written 6′ – see page 64.)

To find the probability that at least one of the numbers is a 6, we need to consider the ways in which this can happen.

The first three rows marked with * are all cases where one (or more) of the cards is a 6 and provide alternative ways of satisfying the condition.

In other words, 'at least one card is a six' corresponds to:

$6, 6$ *or* $6, \overline{6}$ *or* $\overline{6}, 6$

and P(at least one card is a 6)

$$= \left(\frac{1}{8} \times \frac{1}{8}\right) + \left(\frac{1}{8} \times \frac{7}{8}\right) + \left(\frac{7}{8} \times \frac{1}{8}\right) = \frac{15}{64}$$

This example illustrates the important rule that:

> 'or' $\Leftrightarrow$ +

i.e. whenever 'or' occurs in a probability problem it corresponds to *adding* probabilities.

Note: The equivalences 'and' $\Leftrightarrow \times$

and 'or' $\Leftrightarrow$ +

must be used with care, but are good general guidelines to follow.

It should be noted at this point that an alternative way of solving this problem is to use the complement of the event 'at least one card is a six', i.e. 'no card is a six'.

$$\text{P(no card is a 6)} = \text{P}(\overline{6} \text{ and } \overline{6}) = \frac{7}{8} \times \frac{7}{8} = \frac{49}{64}$$

Hence P(at least one card is a 6) $= 1 - \frac{49}{64} = \frac{15}{64}$, as before.

This method of using the complement (and not forgetting to subtract from 1 at the end!) is particularly useful in problems involving the phrase 'at least'.

Example Two cards are drawn randomly from an ordinary pack of playing cards but this time a card is not replaced before the next is removed (*sampling without replacement*). Find the probability that:

(a) The two cards are of the same colour

(b) Just one of the cards is a spade.

Solution (a)

1st draw	*2nd draw*	*Outcome*	*Probability*
R ($\frac{26}{52}$)	R ($\frac{25}{51}$)	RR	$\frac{26}{52} \times \frac{25}{51}$ *
	B ($\frac{26}{51}$)	RB	$\frac{26}{52} \times \frac{26}{51}$
B ($\frac{26}{52}$)	R ($\frac{26}{51}$)	BR	$\frac{26}{52} \times \frac{26}{51}$
	B ($\frac{25}{51}$)	BB	$\frac{26}{52} \times \frac{25}{51}$ *

You should note carefully how the fact of 'not replacing' the first card affects the probabilities at the second draw.

The outcomes marked * correspond to two cards being of the same colour and we have:

$$P\text{ (cards are same colour)} = \frac{26}{52} \times \frac{25}{51} + \frac{26}{52} \times \frac{25}{51}$$
$$= 2 \times \frac{1}{2} \times \frac{25}{51} = \frac{25}{51}$$

(b) The relevant tree diagram is:

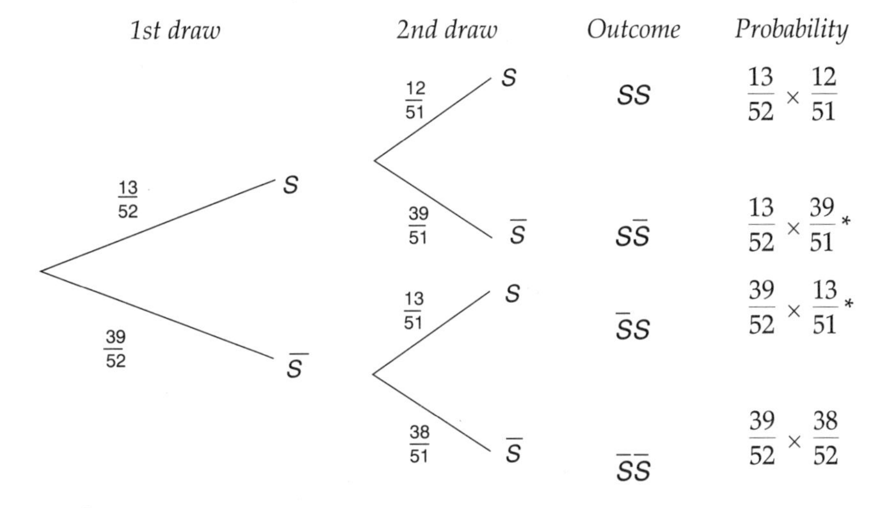

The relevant outcomes are marked * and

$$P\text{ (just one card is a spade)} = \frac{13}{52} \times \frac{39}{51} + \frac{39}{52} \times \frac{13}{51}$$
$$= 2 \times \frac{1}{4} \times \frac{13}{17} = \frac{13}{34}$$

Permutations and combinations

The heading refers to important counting methods which, apart from being useful in their own right, can also be an aid in solving certain types of probability problems.

A **permutation** of some objects is essentially an **arrangement** of them. If we consider say 5 objects then we could arrange them in a row in 5! (= 120) ways. When you see 5!, read 'five factorial'.

Since we could fill the first position in the row in 5 ways, then we would have 4 choices for the second position and so on giving $5 \times 4 \times 3 \times 2 \times 1 = 5!$ ways in all.

Consider now 5 objects, but only three spaces. The first space could be filled in 5 ways, the second in 4 ways and the third in 3 ways giving $5 \times 4 \times 3$ ways altogether.

The number of permutations (or arrangements) of 3 objects from 5 objects is therefore $5 \times 4 \times 3$ which can be written as

$$\frac{5 \times 4 \times 3 \times 2 \times 1}{2 \times 1} \quad \text{or} \quad \frac{5!}{2!}$$

Similarly for 6 objects and 4 spaces this reasoning would give us $\frac{6!}{2!}$.

In general the number of permutations of r distinguishable objects out of n objects is:

$$^nP_r = \frac{n!}{(n-r)!}$$

Indistinguishable objects

It may be that some objects are indistinguishable. For example, how many permutations are there of the letters *ABBC* where it is not possible to distinguish between the two *B*'s?

To answer this question, pretend for a moment that we can distinguish the *B*'s by labelling them B_1, B_2. Then the arrangements would be 4! in number

i.e. $A\ B_1\ B_2\ C$, $A\ B_1\ C\ B_2$, etc.

but the list would also include $A\ B_2\ B_1\ C$, $A\ B_2\ C\ B_1$ and so on. If the *B*'s were not distinguished, these would be the same arrangements, namely $A\ B\ B\ C$ and $A\ B\ C\ B$. We have an answer which is two times too large.

The correct number is $\frac{4!}{2!}$.

If we had 9 objects where 4 were indistinguishable, we would similarly get $\frac{9!}{4!}$.

We could have objects $A\ B\ B\ B\ C\ D\ D\ D\ D$.

The result would be $\frac{9!}{3!\,4!}$ where the factor 3! corresponds to the *B*'s and 4! corresponds to the *D*'s.

In general for n objects, r of which are the same, we have $\frac{n!}{r!}$ permutations and as can be seen above the result extends.

Example Find the number of arrangements of the letters of the word:

S T A T I S T I C S

Solution We have 10 letters and this includes:

3 S's
3 T's
1 A
1 C
2 I's

giving $\frac{10!}{3!\,3!\,2!} = 50\,400$

Example Find the number of ways in which 11 boys can stand in a row if two of them refuse to stand next to each other.

Solution This problem is difficult to solve directly.

The following approach is useful when a restriction is involved. Consider the number of arrangements if the boys are stuck together as a single entity. Call them Andy and Bill.

(AB) (remaining 9 boys)

How many arrangements?

There are now 10 objects altogether giving 10! arrangements.

However for each of these we could also have the equivalent but with A and B in reverse order, i.e.

(BA) (remaining 9 boys)

Hence in all, there are $2 \times 10!$ ways of arranging the boys so that Andy and Bill are next to each other. The total number of arrangements without restriction is 11!

The difference between them is those arrangements where the boys are separated.

$$\begin{aligned} \text{Hence number of arrangements} &= 11! - (2 \times 10!) \\ &= 10!\,(11 - 2) \\ &= 9 \times 10! \\ &= 32\,659\,200 \end{aligned}$$

A *combination* of some objects is equivalent to a **selection**. As an example consider the following:

Out of a collection of 5 novels by my favourite author, I would like to choose 3 to take on holiday. How many choices do I have?

In this case it is not too difficult to list the selections provided we are systematic.

Call the books $A \; B \; C \; D \; E$

then the choices are:

A B C	A C D	B C D	C D E
A B D	A C E	B C E	
A B E	A D E	B D E	

i.e. 10 in all.

Now if order had been important, for each of these selections or combinations there would be 6 arrangements or permutations of each.

So to arrive at the number of combinations we need to reduce the number of permutations by the factor 6 (= 3!)

Hence ${}^5C_3$ the number of combinations of 3 out of 5 is given by

$$ {}^5C_3 = \frac{{}^5P_3}{3!} $$

$$ = \frac{5!}{2!\,3!} \quad \left(\text{using the fact that } {}^5P_3 = \frac{5!}{2!}\right) $$

$$ = 10 $$

Generalising for a selection of r things out of n distinguishable things we have:

$$ {}^nC_r = \frac{n!}{(n-r)!\,r!} $$

Note: an alternative and commonly used notation for ${}^nC_r$ is $\binom{n}{r}$.

Example 3 people have to be chosen from a group of 8 as a committee. How many selections are possible.

Solution

$$ {}^8C_3 = \frac{8!}{5!\,3!} = 56 $$

Example

In the National Lottery, 6 numbers have to be selected from 49 numbers to scoop the jackpot.

(a) How many possible selections are there?

If one ticket is bought, what is the probability of winning?

Solution

(a) There are ${}^{49}C_6$ possible selections

$$\begin{aligned} {}^{49}C_6 &= \frac{49!}{43!\,6!} \\ &= 13{,}983{,}816 \end{aligned}$$

(b) The probability of winning with one entry is $\frac{1}{13\,983\,816}$

or approximately 1 in 14 million.

A slightly more difficult problem arises if we are selecting from a set of objects which are not all different.

Example

How many selections of 3 letters are there from the word:

P R O B A B L E

Solution

Consider the types of selection as:

2 B's + 1 other
1 B + 2 others
0 B's + 3 others

since it is the double B which causes the problem.

2B's and 1 other is 6 ways
(since the extra one is chosen from P R O A L E)
1B and 2 others is ${}^6C_2$ ways
(since we now have to choose 2 from P R O A L E)
0 B's and 3 others is ${}^6C_3$
(since now we choose 3 from P R O A L E)

Total number of ways is $6 + {}^6C_2 + {}^6C_3$

$= 6 + 15 + 20$

$= 41$

Example Find the probability that a hand of 13 cards dealt from an ordinary pack will contain at least 11 spades.

Solution We need to work out the probabilities of:

11 spades
12 spades
13 spades

and then add these.

$$P(11\text{ spades}) = \frac{{}^{13}C_{11} \times {}^{39}C_2}{{}^{52}C_{13}}$$

since we have to select 11 out of 13 spades and 2 out of 39 other cards and this out of a total of ${}^{52}C_{13}$ possible selections of 13 out of 52.

$$P(12\text{ spades}) = \frac{{}^{13}C_{12} \times {}^{39}C_1}{{}^{52}C_{13}}$$

$$P(13\text{ spades}) = \frac{{}^{13}C_{13} \times {}^{39}C_0}{{}^{52}C_{13}}$$

Hence P (11 or more spades)

$$= \frac{({}^{13}C_{11} \times {}^{39}C_2) + ({}^{13}C_{12} \times {}^{39}C_1) + ({}^{13}C_{13} \times {}^{39}C_0)}{{}^{52}C_{13}}$$

$= 9.2 \times 10^{-8}$ (highly unlikely to happen)

Conditional probability and independence

A card is selected from an ordinary pack of cards. What is the probability that it is a king? The answer is clearly $\frac{4}{52} = \frac{1}{13}$.

Suppose however there is some additional information available about the card selected. Suppose, for example, that it is known to be a court card (i.e. a king, queen or jack). What is the probability of it being a king if it is known to be a court card?

The extra information increases the probability to $\frac{4}{12} = \frac{1}{3}$ since there are only now 12 possibilities for the card. In other words the sample space has been reduced to a set containing only 12 members.

Suppose instead it was known to be a black card. How would this affect the probability of it being a king? The sample space is now reduced to 26 cards, but the number of possible kings has been reduced to 2 since it is known that the chosen card is black.

$$\text{Hence P(king given black card)} = \frac{2}{26} = \frac{1}{13}$$

This is the same as the original result where no extra information was given. Sometimes extra information doesn't make a difference therefore to the final probability.

The solution where extra information is provided in a problem is referred to as a *conditional* probability and such problems are often written in the form 'what is the probability of some event *given* some extra information'.

We write $P(A \mid B)$ for the probability of event A, given that B is known to have occurred and this is calculated from the formula:

$$P(A \mid B) = \frac{P(A \cap B)}{P(B)}$$

The Venn diagram, Figure 5.5, provides a justification for this formula.

Figure 5.5

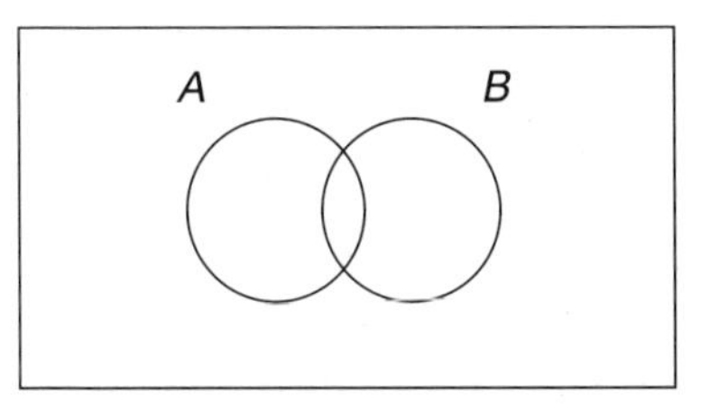

B is given (has occurred) so that we know we must be within that circle. What is the chance that A has happened given that we are in circle B? It will equal the proportion of the circle B taken up by A

i.e. $\dfrac{P(A \cap B)}{P(B)}$

Effectively, B becomes the new sample space.

Example For the eight numbered cards a card is selected. What is the probability it is higher than 4 given that it is even?

Solution This is a fairly simple problem to solve and can probably most easily be done by counting methods. However the solution presented will use the formula as it illustrates a useful technique.

Let A be the event: 'The card is higher than 4.'

Let B be the event: 'The card is even.'

Then $P(A \mid B)$ is what is required

i.e. $\dfrac{P(A \cap B)}{P(B)}$

Now $P(B) = \dfrac{1}{2}$ i.e. $\left(\dfrac{n(\{2, 4, 6, 8\})}{n(\{1, 2, 3, 4, 5, 6, 7, 8\})}\right)$

$A \cap B$ is the event 'higher than 4 *and* even' and is satisfied by 6 and 8 only.

So $P(A \cap B) = \dfrac{2}{8}$

$$\Rightarrow P(A \mid B) = \frac{\frac{2}{8}}{\frac{1}{2}} = \frac{2}{8} \times \frac{2}{1} = \frac{1}{2}$$

Example Two cards are drawn from an ordinary pack without replacement. Find the probability that the first card is a spade given that the second card is not a spade.

Solution Let A = '1st card is a spade'

Let B = '2nd card is not a spade'

then $P(A \mid B) = \dfrac{P(A \cap B)}{P(B)}$ as usual.

$A \cap B$ is the event '1st card is a spade and 2nd card is not a spade' and can be abbreviated $S\bar{S}$ using the notation introduced earlier.

$$P(S\bar{S}) = \frac{13}{52} \times \frac{39}{51} = \frac{13}{68} = P(A \cap B)$$

$P(B)$ is obtained by considering the ways in which the second card can turn out to be a spade and a tree diagram helps to find that:

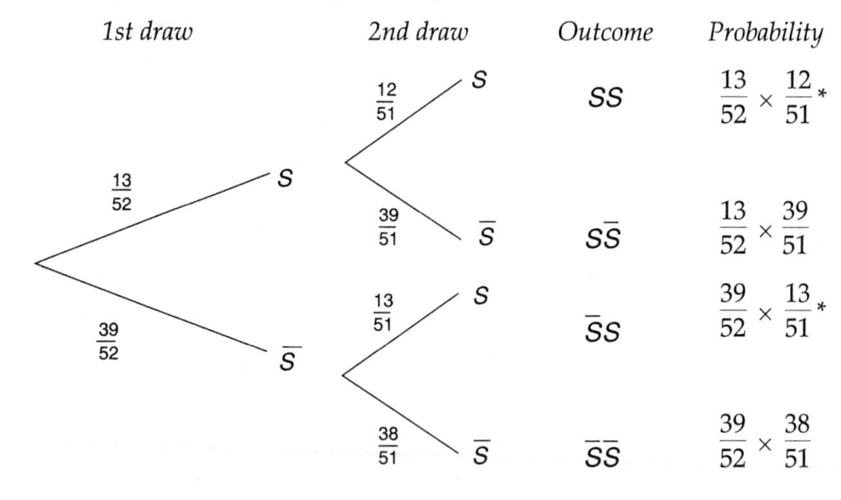

The relevant outcomes are marked * and so:

$$P(B) = \frac{13}{52} \times \frac{12}{51} + \frac{39}{52} \times \frac{13}{51} = \frac{1}{4}$$

$$\Rightarrow P(A \mid B) = \frac{\frac{13}{68}}{\frac{1}{4}} = \frac{13}{17}$$

We met an example earlier where the information about B did not affect the probability of A.

i.e. we had $P(A \mid B) = P(A)$

If this property holds then A is said to be **independent of** B. It is possible to show that if A is independent of B then the converse is also true, i.e. that B is independent of A. This means that we can talk about independent events rather than the independence of one event from another. So from now on if $P(A \mid B) = P(A)$ we call the events A and B independent.

Although the definition of independence involves a statement about a conditional probability, in practice, the following consequence is much simpler to use in problem solving.

$$P(A \mid B) = P(A)$$

$$\Rightarrow \frac{P(A \cap B)}{P(B)} = P(A)$$

$$\Rightarrow P(A \cap B) = P(A) \times P(B)$$

It should be noted that this idea has been used implicitly in several problems in this section. We now have a more precise idea of when multiplying probabilities is legitimate. The simple multiplication rule stated earlier can only be used when events are independent.

In all the situations in which it has so far been used, independence was assumed on the grounds that the events being considered were physically independent. For example, in drawing two cards from a pack with replacement, the result of the first selection can have no influence on the outcome of the second selection. These activities are independent of each other and so the multiplication rule can be used.

To conclude, events A and B are independent if:

$$P(A \cap B) = P(A) \times P(B)$$

and we can use this both ways. Namely, if we are given that the events are independent, then it is legitimate to multiply their probabilities according to this rule. Conversely, if this rule applies numerically, then we can safely conclude that the events are independent.

Example Two dice are thrown, one green and the other blue. A is the event 'the green die shows a 3', B is the event 'the sum of the scores is 8'. Are A and B independent?

Solution

$$P(A) = \frac{6}{36} \qquad P(B) = \frac{5}{36}$$

$$A \cap B = \{(3, 5)\} \Rightarrow P(A \cap B) = \frac{1}{36}$$

$$P(A) \times P(B) = \frac{6}{36} \times \frac{5}{36} = \frac{5}{216} \neq P(A \cap B)$$

Hence the events are dependent.

Example Given that $P(A) = \frac{1}{3}$, $P(B) = \frac{2}{5}$ and $P(A \cup B) = \frac{3}{5}$, find the values of $P(A \cap B)$, $P(A \mid B)$ and $P(B \mid A)$. Are A and B independent?

Solution We use $P(A \cup B) = P(A) + (P(B) - P(A \cap B)$ to find $P(A \cap B)$

$$\frac{3}{5} = \frac{1}{3} + \frac{2}{5} - P(A \cap B)$$

$$\Rightarrow P(A \cap B) = \frac{2}{15}$$

$$\text{Now } P(A \mid B) = \frac{P(A \cap B)}{P(B)} = \frac{\frac{2}{15}}{\frac{2}{5}} = \frac{1}{3}$$

$$P(B \mid A) = \frac{P(B \cap A)}{P(A)} = \frac{\frac{2}{15}}{\frac{1}{3}} = \frac{2}{5}$$

$$P(A) \times P(B) = \frac{1}{3} \times \frac{2}{5} = \frac{2}{15} = P(A \cap B)$$

so A and B are independent.

When A and B are independent, we're familiar with the simple multiplication rule:

$$P(A \cap B) = P(A) \times P(B)$$

When A and B are *not* independent, the conditional probabilities $P(A \mid B)$ and $P(B \mid A)$ are both measures of their dependence on each other. These probabilities can then be used to modify the multiplication rule.

$$P(A \mid B) = \frac{P(A \cap B)}{P(B)}$$

Multiplying both sides by $P(B)$ gives:

$$P(A \cap B) = P(B) \times P(A \mid B)$$

In the same way, $P(B \mid A) = \dfrac{P(A \cap B)}{P(A)}$

$$\Rightarrow \quad P(A \cap B) = P(A) \times P(B \mid A)$$

So:
$$P(A \cap B) = P(A) \times P(B \mid A) = P(B) \times P(A \mid B)$$

Example Given that $P(A) = \frac{2}{5}$ and $P(B \mid A) = \frac{1}{3}$, find $P(A \cap B)$.

Solution

$$P(A \cap B) = P(A) \times P(B \mid A) = \frac{2}{5} \times \frac{1}{3} = \frac{2}{15}.$$

Note: When A and B are independent, $P(A \mid B) = P(A)$ [because B doesn't affect the probability of A] and $P(B \mid A) = P(B)$.

Then both versions of this multiplication rule become the simpler, more familiar rule, e.g.

$$P(A \cap B) = P(A) \times P(B \mid A) = P(A) \times P(B)$$

You should now be able to answer Exercises 3–12 on pages 79–81.

EXERCISES

1 A and B are two events such that:

$$P(A) = 0.6,\ P(B) = 0.2 \text{ and } P(A \cap B) = 0.1$$

Find:

(a) $P(A' \cap B)$,

(b) the probability that exactly one of A and B will occur.

2 A die and three coins are simultaneously tossed. Find the probability of the event 'at least one head and a score of more than 4'.

3 An urn contains 3 red, 4 white and 5 blue discs. Three discs are selected at random from the urn.

Find the probability that:

(a) all three discs are the same colour, if the selection is with replacement,

(b) all three discs are of different colours, if the selection is without replacement.

4 Container 1 has 3 red balls and 4 blue balls in it. Container 2 has 5 red balls and 2 blue balls in it. A ball is taken from container 1 and placed in container 2. If a ball is now selected randomly from container 1 what is the probability that it is red?

5 How many three digit numbers can be formed using the digits 1, 2, 3, 4, 5, where each digit can be used only once? How many of them are odd?

6 In a group of six students, 4 are female and 2 are male. Determine how many committees of 3 members can be formed containing 1 male and 2 females.

7 A child has a bag containing 12 sweets of which 3 are yellow, 5 are green and 4 are red. When the child wants to eat one of the sweets, a random selection is made from the bag and the chosen sweet is then eaten before the next random selection is made.

(a) Find the probability that the child does not select a yellow sweet in the first two selections.

(b) Find the probability that there is at least one yellow sweet in the first two selections.

(c) Find the probability that the fourth sweet selected is yellow, given that the first two sweets selected were red ones.

8 A and B are two independent events such that:

$$\mathrm{P}(A) = \alpha \text{ and } \mathrm{P}(A \cup B) = \beta,\ \beta > \alpha$$

Show that:

$$\mathrm{P}(B) = \frac{\beta - \alpha}{1 - \alpha}$$

9 In a large group of people it is known that 10% have a hot breakfast, 20% have a hot lunch and 25% have a hot breakfast or a hot lunch. Find the probability that a person chosen at random from this group

(a) has a hot breakfast and a hot lunch,

(b) has a hot lunch, given that the person chosen had a hot breakfast.

10 A and B are two independent events such that $\mathrm{P}(A) = 0.2$ and $\mathrm{P}(B) = 0.15$.

Evaluate the following probabilities:

(a) $\mathrm{P}(A \mid B)$

(b) $\mathrm{P}(A \cap B)$

(c) $\mathrm{P}(A \cup B)$

11 Team A has a probability $\frac{2}{3}$ of winning whenever it plays.

Given that A plays 4 games, find the probability that A wins more than half of the games.

12 A house is infested with mice and to combat this the householder acquired four cats. Albert, Belinda, Khalid and Poon. The householder observes that only half of the creatures caught are mice. A fifth are voles and the rest are birds.

20% of the catches are made by Albert, 45% by Belinda, 10% by Khalid and 25% by Poon.

(a) The probability of a catch being a mouse, a bird or a vole is independent of whether or not it is made by Albert. What is the probability of a randomly selected catch being a

(i) mouse caught by Albert,

(ii) bird not caught by Albert?

(b) Belinda's catches are equally likely to be a mouse, a bird or a vole. What is the probability of a randomly selected catch being a mouse caught by Belinda?

(c) The probability of a randomly selected catch being a mouse caught by Khalid is 0.05. What is the probability that a catch made by Khalid is a mouse?

(d) Given that the probability that a randomly selected catch is a mouse caught by Poon is 0.2 verify that the probability of a randomly selected catch being a mouse is 0.5.

(e) What is the probability that a catch which is a mouse was made by Belinda?

[AEB 1993]

SUMMARY

Now you have completed this section you should understand the basics of probability theory. In particular you should realise that there are two basic rules for dealing with simple probability problems, the addition rule and the multiplication rule:

- The general addition rule, applying to situations of the form 'either ... or ...' is

  $$P(A \cup B) = P(A) + P(B) - P(A \cap B)$$

  where $P(A \cap B)$ is zero only if A and B are mutually exclusive.

- The general multiplication rule, applying to situations of the form 'both ... and ...' is

  $$P(A \cap B) = P(A) \,.\, P(B \mid A)$$

  and this reduces to

  $$P(A \cap B) = P(A) \,.\, P(B)$$

  only if A and B are independent.

You should also now be able to understand and use:

- tree diagrams and Venn diagrams in problem-solving
- simple permutations and combinations.

SECTION

6

Random variables

INTRODUCTION

In the last section we examined the basic principles of probability. In this section we introduce the concept of random variables and investigate their characteristics. We also examine the concept of expected value. You will need to be familiar with integral calculus for this section.

By the end of this section you should be able to:

- understand what is meant by a random variable
- distinguish between a discrete and a continuous random variable
- understand what is meant by a probability density function and the distribution function
- calculate and interpret an expected value and a variance.

Random variables as models

Random variables provide us with models for data and form the link between probability and statistics. In this section we look at the general properties of random variables. In Sections 7 and 8 we will look at some particular random variables which are used frequently to model data arising in a wide range of situations. One of the major problems of statistics is to provide good models for data as these can be used to make predictions and possibly help in formulating general theories about the situations being considered.

Just as there are essentially two forms in which data can occur, discrete and continuous, there are also two different types of random variable. We start by considering the simpler of these.

Discrete random variables

Definition: Suppose X is a variable quantity which takes n discrete values x_1, x_2, ... x_n and further that it takes these values with probabilities p_1, p_2, ... p_n, then if $p_1 + p_2 + \ldots + p_n = 1$, X is called a **discrete random variable**.

It may be that n is infinite, in which case we would require:

$$\sum_{i=1}^{\infty} p_i = 1$$

At this stage, we must introduce what will strike you as a strange convention, unlike anything you will have come across elsewhere in maths.

As in our definition above, we shall use *capital letters* to name random variables – X, Y, Z – but we shall use the corresponding *lower case letters* for particular values of these random variables.

So x or x_i can both be used for particular values of the random variable X.

This explains the strange notation $P(X = x)$ – the probability that the random variable X takes the particular value x.

Example

Consider the experiment of tossing a coin three times and noting the number of tails shown. Show that X – the number of tails shown – is a discrete random variable.

Solution

We have the following outcomes which are mutually exclusive and exhaustive:

Outcome (x)   *Number of tails*
0
1
2
3

We need to show that:

$$\sum_{x=0}^{n} P(X = x) = 1$$

Letting H denote heads and T tails we have for:

$$\begin{aligned}
P(X = 0) &= P(H \cap H \cap H) = \tfrac{1}{2} \times \tfrac{1}{2} \times \tfrac{1}{2} = \tfrac{1}{8} \\
P(X = 1) &= P(H \cap H \cap T) + P(H \cap T \cap H) + P(T \cap H \cap H) \\
&= (\tfrac{1}{2} \times \tfrac{1}{2} \times \tfrac{1}{2}) + (\tfrac{1}{2} \times \tfrac{1}{2} \times \tfrac{1}{2}) + (\tfrac{1}{2} \times \tfrac{1}{2} \times \tfrac{1}{2}) = \tfrac{3}{8} \\
P(X = 2) &= P(H \cap T \cap T) + P(T \cap H \cap T) + P(T \cap T \cap H) \\
&= (\tfrac{1}{2} \times \tfrac{1}{2} \times \tfrac{1}{2}) + (\tfrac{1}{2} \times \tfrac{1}{2} \times \tfrac{1}{2}) + (\tfrac{1}{2} \times \tfrac{1}{2} \times \tfrac{1}{2}) = \tfrac{3}{8} \\
P(X = 3) &= P(T \cap T \cap T) = \tfrac{1}{2} \times \tfrac{1}{2} \times \tfrac{1}{2} = \tfrac{1}{8}
\end{aligned}$$

Note that we have to be careful to notice that the same outcome (e.g. two heads) can occur in a number of different ways.

Therefore:

$$\sum_{x=0}^{3} P(X = x) = \frac{1}{8} + \frac{3}{8} + \frac{3}{8} + \frac{1}{8} = 1$$

confirming that X is a discrete random variable.

This discrete random variable X, the number of tails when 3 coins are tossed, can be summarised in the following table, called its **probability distribution**.

x	0	1	2	3
$P(X = x)$	$\frac{1}{8}$	$\frac{3}{8}$	$\frac{3}{8}$	$\frac{1}{8}$

where the first row lists the outcomes and the second row lists the probabilities for each of the outcomes.

This random variable would be a good model for the experiment providing the coin were unbiased.

The following example illustrates that discrete random variables can be defined by functions.

Example

Consider the function defined as follows:

$$\begin{array}{ll} p(x) = kx^2 & x = 1, 2, 3 \\ p(x) = k(7 - x)^2 & x = 4, 5, 6 \\ p(x) = 0 & \text{otherwise} \end{array}$$

Now if $p(x)$ stands for $P(X = x)$ then for a certain value of k, which we can determine, the function will define a discrete random variable.

The problem is to find the value of k.

Solution

Using the appropriate part of the function we have:

$$\begin{array}{lllll} p(1) = k \times 1^2 & = k & = P(X = 1) \\ p(2) = k \times 2^2 & = 4k & = P(X = 2) \\ p(3) = k \times 3^2 & = 9k & = P(X = 3) \\ p(4) = k\,(7 - 4)^2 & = 9k & = P(X = 4) \\ p(5) = k\,(7 - 5)^2 & = 4k & = P(X = 5) \\ p(6) = k(7 - 6)^2 & = k & = P(X = 6) \end{array}$$

We require that these probabilities should add up to 1.

$$\sum_{x=1}^{6} p(x) = 1$$

$$\Rightarrow k + 4k + 9k + 9k + 4k + k = 1$$
$$\Rightarrow 28k = 1$$
$$\Rightarrow k = \frac{1}{28}$$

We can now complete the probability distribution for the random variable X:

x	1	2	3	4	5	6
$P(X = x)$	$\frac{1}{28}$	$\frac{4}{28}$	$\frac{9}{28}$	$\frac{9}{28}$	$\frac{4}{28}$	$\frac{1}{28}$

Probability function and cumulative distribution function

The probability function of a discrete random variable, X, is a function that assigns probabilities to each of the values that X can take. It can be written as $P(X = x)$, that is, the probability that X takes on the specific value x. It can normally be obtained from a tabulation of the probabilities (as in the example of tossing a coin) or from an algebraic function (as in the last example).

The cumulative distribution function of a discrete random variable X is defined as:

$$F(x_0) = P(X \leq x_0) = \sum_{x \leq x_0} p(x)$$

and is a new function formed from the probability function by accumulating the probability up to some value x_0 (rather like the cumulative frequencies from Section 2).

Example The random variable X, is the total score obtained when two dice are thrown. Find:

(a) The probability distribution of X

(b) The cumulative distribution function $F(x)$

(c) Say what is meant by $F(6)$ and $F(12)$

Solution (a) The possible outcomes range from $X = 2$ to $X = 12$, but the outcomes are not equally likely as, for example, there are more ways of scoring a total of 6 than a total of 2.

Proceeding systematically the following probabilities are obtained.

x	2	3	4	5	6	7	8	9	10	11	12
$P(X = x)$	$\frac{1}{36}$	$\frac{2}{36}$	$\frac{3}{36}$	$\frac{4}{36}$	$\frac{5}{36}$	$\frac{6}{36}$	$\frac{5}{36}$	$\frac{4}{36}$	$\frac{3}{36}$	$\frac{2}{36}$	$\frac{1}{36}$

where for example the value for $x = 4$ is obtained by counting up the possible ways of obtaining a total of 4 which are (3, 1), (2, 2), (1, 3).

There are 36 possible outcomes altogether. The table is the probability distribution.

(b) For the cumulative distribution function we get:

x_0	2	3	4	5	6	7	8	9	10	11	12
$P(X \le x_0)$	$\frac{1}{36}$	$\frac{3}{36}$	$\frac{6}{36}$	$\frac{10}{36}$	$\frac{15}{36}$	$\frac{21}{36}$	$\frac{26}{36}$	$\frac{30}{36}$	$\frac{33}{36}$	$\frac{35}{36}$	$\frac{36}{36}$

where for example the value for $x_0 = 4$ is obtained by adding all the probabilities up to $x = 4$ in the table from part (a).

so $P(X \le 4) = \frac{1}{36} + \frac{2}{36} + \frac{3}{36} = \frac{6}{36} = F(4)$

(c) $F(6) = \frac{15}{36}$ and equals $P(X \le 6)$

$F(12) = \frac{36}{36}$ and equals $P(X \le 12)$

Note that $F(12) = 1$ and this should be the case as all of the probabilities are added at this point (all scores being ≤ 12 for this random variable).

You should now be able to complete Exercises 1–3 on page 106.

Continuous random variables

Discrete random variables are used to model situations in which discrete data is obtained. These quite often refer to situations which start with the phrase 'X is the number of …'; in other words, they refer to situations in which counting is taking place.

Continuous random variables are used to model data sets which are continuous in nature and are usually the result of making a measurement, e.g. heights of people or the time taken to complete a journey.

Continuous data is usually grouped into intervals and is represented graphically by a histogram where the areas of columns correspond to the frequencies within each interval. The mid-points of these columns can be joined by a continuous curve, thereby bringing out the continuous nature of the data even more. Correspondingly the important features of continuous random variables are:

(a) that they can be represented graphically by continuous curves

(b) that areas under the curve correspond to probabilities.

Because continuous random variables correspond to continuous curves, they are defined in terms of continuous functions called **probability density functions**.

> A probability density function (PDF) defined over the interval $a \le x \le b$ is a function f(x) with the properties
>
> (i) $\int_a^b f(x)\,dx = 1$ (ii) $f(x) \ge 0$ for all $a \le x \le b$

This amounts to saying that all the probabilities sum to 1 and all probabilities are positive or zero and correspond to similar results for discrete random variables.

It may be that a or b (or both) are infinite and indeed this is the case with the most important continuous distribution (the normal distribution – described in Section 8).

Finding probabilities for continuous random variables amounts to doing integrations as illustrated in example 1.

Example

The continuous variable X has a PDF given by:

$$f(x) = \begin{cases} \frac{1}{5}(4x+3) & \text{for } 0 \le x \le 1 \\ 0 & \text{elsewhere} \end{cases}$$

(a) Verify that $f(x)$ is a PDF

(b) Find $P(0 \le X \le 0.75)$

Solution

(a) We must show that $\int_0^1 f(x)\,dx = 1$

as this is required by the definition of a PDF.

We have $\int_0^1 \frac{1}{5}(4x+3)\,dx = \frac{1}{5}\left[2x^2 + 3x\right]_0^1$

$$= \frac{1}{5}(5-0) = 1$$

So $f(x)$ behaves like a PDF and we conclude that X is a continuous random variable.

(b) $P(0 \le X \le 0.75) = \int_0^{0.75} \frac{1}{5}(4x+3)\ dx$

$$= \frac{1}{5}\left[2x^2 + 3x\right]_0^{0.75} = 0.675$$

Therefore the probability that X takes a value between 0 and 0.75 is 0.675.

Example

A continuous distribution is defined by the PDF:

$$f(x) = \begin{cases} c\left(\frac{6}{5}x^2 + 10\right) & \text{for } 0 \le x \le 5 \text{ where } c \text{ is a constant} \\ 0 & \text{elsewhere} \end{cases}$$

(a) Find c.

(b) Determine the probabilities for the intervals 0 to 1, 1 to 2, 2 to 3, 3 to 4 and 4 to 5.

Solution

(a) $\int_0^5 f(x)\ dx = 1$ (The basic requirement for a PDF)

$$\Rightarrow \int_0^5 c\left(\frac{6}{5}x^2 + 10\right)dx = 1$$

$$\Rightarrow c\left[\frac{2}{5}x^3 + 10x\right]_0^5 = 1$$

giving $c\left[0.4(5^3) + 50\right] = 1$ giving $c = \frac{1}{100}$

(b) We now need to evaluate $\int_a^b f(x)\ dx$ for the given intervals:

The first gives $\frac{1}{100}\left[\frac{2x^3}{5} + 10x\right]_0^1$ using the known value for c, and which on evaluation gives 0.104. That is, the probability that X takes a value in the interval 0 to 1 is 0.104.

Similarly for the other intervals we have:

$\frac{1}{100}\left[\frac{2}{5}x^3 + 10x\right]_1^2$ giving $0.232 - 0.104 = 0.128$

$\frac{1}{100}\left[\frac{2}{5}x^3 + 10x\right]_2^3$ giving $0.408 - 0.232 = 0.176$

$$\frac{1}{100}\left[\frac{2}{5}x^3 + 10x\right]_3^4 \qquad \text{giving } 0.656 - 0.408 = 0.248$$

$$\frac{1}{100}\left[\frac{2}{5}x^3 + 10x\right]_4^5 \qquad \text{giving } 1.000 - 0.656 = 0.344$$

Double-checking shows us that if we sum these probabilities they total to 1.000. We shall return to examine specific probability distributions and their properties in more detail in the next section(s).

An important property of continuous random variables which follows from the property

$$\int_a^a f(x)\,dx = 0$$

is that $P(X = a) = 0$ for all a.

A consequence of this property is that, for example:

$$P(X \le a) = P(X < a)$$

This property only holds for continuous random variables, however.

You should now be able to complete Exercises 5–6 on pages 105–106.

The cumulative distribution function

If X is a continuous random variable with PDF

$$\begin{cases} f(x) & a \le x \le b \\ 0 & \text{elsewhere} \end{cases}$$

then we can define a new function $F(x)$ called the **cumulative distribution function** (CDF) by the following:

$$F(x) = \int_a^x f(t)\,dt = P(X \le x)$$

The usefulness of this function is best illustrated by an example.

Example

Random variable X has PDF given by:

$$f(x) = \begin{cases} \frac{3}{4}x(2 - x) & 0 \le x \le 2 \\ 0 & \text{otherwise} \end{cases}$$

Find $F(x)$, the CDF of this random variable,

Find also $F(0)$, $F(1)$ and $F(2)$ and give a interpretation of these values.

Solution According to the definition:

$$F(x) = P(X \le x) = \int_0^x \frac{3}{4} t\,(2-t)\,dt$$

(Note: t is a dummy variable in this integration, which is introduced to avoid confusion with the x that appears as the upper limit of the integral.)

$$\Rightarrow F(x) = \frac{3}{4}\int_0^x (2t - t^2)\,dt$$

$$\Rightarrow F(x) = \frac{3}{4}\left[\frac{2t^2}{2} - \frac{t^3}{3}\right]_0^x$$

$$\Rightarrow F(x) = \frac{3}{4}\left[\left(x^2 - \frac{x^3}{3}\right) - (0)\right]$$

$$\Rightarrow F(x) = \frac{3}{4}x^2 - \frac{x^3}{4}$$

$$F(0) = 0$$

$$F(1) = \frac{3}{4} - \frac{1}{4} = \frac{1}{2}$$

$$F(2) = \frac{3}{4}(4) - \frac{8}{4} = 1$$

The interpretations are:

$$P(X \le 0) = 0$$

$$P(X \le 1) = \frac{1}{2}$$

$$P(X \le 2) = 1$$

and these results make sense when we consider the graph of the PDF (Figure 6.1)

Figure 6.1

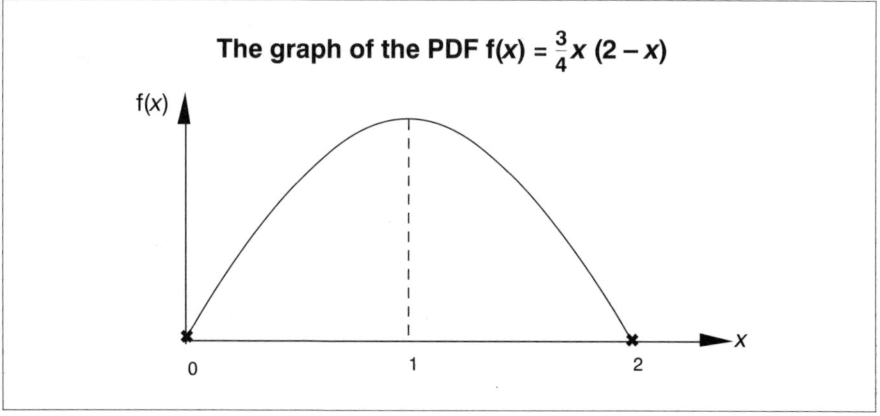

There is no probability below the value $x = 0$.

By symmetry exactly half the probability is to the left of $x = 1$.

All of the probability is taken up by the value $x = 2$.

It turns out to be useful if the CDF takes a value for every x that is input and the complete definition of F(x) in this example is:

$$F(x) = \begin{cases} 0 & x < 0 \\ \frac{3}{4}x^2 - \frac{x^3}{4} & 0 \le x \le 2 \\ 1 & x \ge 2 \end{cases}$$

The graph of F(x) is shown in Figure 6.2.

Figure 6.2

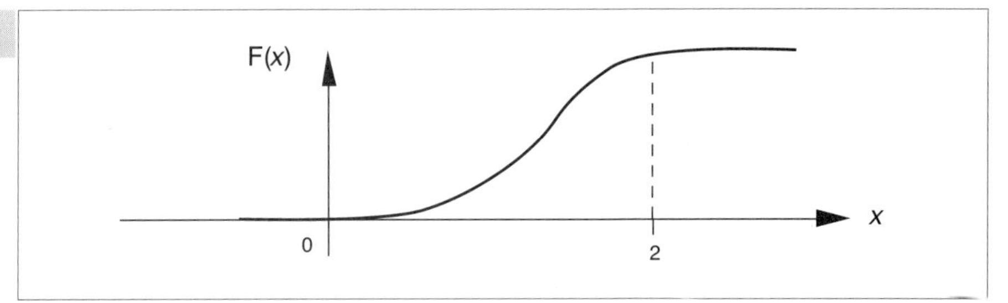

We have seen that the CDF is obtained from the PDF by integrating

i.e. $$F(x) = \int_a^x f(t)\,dt$$

and the value $F(x_0)$ for example gives the accumulated probability up to the value $x = x_0$.

Because of the relationship between differentiating and integrating we can obtain the PDF from the CDF by differentiating

i.e. $$f(x) = \frac{d}{dx}(F(x))$$

You should check that this works with the example just completed.

You should now be able to answer Exercises 6–7 on page 107.

Expected value

Given the similarities between a frequency distribution and a probability distribution, it may be apparent that there should also be similarities between some of the statistical measures we used in earlier sections on data and the equivalent statistics for a probability distribution. In probability we focus on two such measures: the mean and the variance of the distribution, although they are more usually referred to in terms of expectation.

If X is a discrete random variable with probability distribution as in the table shown

x	x_1	x_2	...	x_n
$P(X = x)$	p_1	p_2	...	p_n

then the expectation of X is defined as

$$\begin{aligned} E(X) &= x_1 p_1 + x_2 p_2 + \ldots + x_n p_n \\ &= \sum_{i=1}^{i=n} x_i p_i \end{aligned}$$

For a continuous random variable with PDF $f(x)$ taking non-zero values only on the interval $[a, b]$ the corresponding definition is

$$E(X) = \int_a^b x\, f(x)\, dx$$

The expectation (in both cases) is a measure of the theoretical average value of X and corresponds to $\bar{x}$ for data.

An alternative notation for $E(X)$ is μ (pronounced 'mu').

Example Let X = the outcome when an ordinary die is thrown.

Then X has the distribution shown:

x	1	2	3	4	5	6
$P(X = x)$	$\frac{1}{6}$	$\frac{1}{6}$	$\frac{1}{6}$	$\frac{1}{6}$	$\frac{1}{6}$	$\frac{1}{6}$

$$E(X) = 1 \times \frac{1}{6} + 2 \times \frac{1}{6} + 3 \times \frac{1}{6} + 4 \times \frac{1}{6} + 5 \times \frac{1}{6} + 6 \times \frac{1}{6}$$

$$\Rightarrow E(X) = 3.5$$

If you were to throw a die a large number of times (or simulate this activity using random numbers) and find the average of your results it would be close to 3.5. The bigger the number of throws or simulations the closer the average result would be to the value of 3.5.

$E(X) = 3.5$ is the theoretical (long-term) average for the experiment.

Example (a) A discrete random variable X has the probability function

$$P(X = x) = \begin{cases} kx^2 & x = 0, 1, 2, 3 \\ 0 & \text{otherwise} \end{cases}$$

Find the values of k and $E(X)$

(b) A continuous random variable, X, has the probability density function, $f(x)$ given by:

$$f(x) = \begin{cases} kx^2 & 0 \le x \le 3 \\ 0 & \text{otherwise} \end{cases}$$

Find the values of k and $E(X)$

Solution

(a) To find the value of k use the fact that the probabilities must add to 1

$$\begin{aligned} P(X=0) &= k \times 0^2 = 0 \\ P(X=1) &= k \times 1^2 = k \\ P(X=2) &= k \times 2^2 = 4k \\ P(X=3) &= k \times 3^2 = 9k \end{aligned}$$

$$\text{Sum} = 14k = 1 \Rightarrow k = \frac{1}{14}$$

For E(X) we have:

$E(X) = \Sigma x P(X = x)$ for all x

$$\begin{aligned} x = 0 \quad & p(x) = 0 \\ x = 1 \quad & p(x) = \frac{1}{14} \\ x = 2 \quad & p(x) = \frac{4}{14} \\ x = 3 \quad & p(x) = \frac{9}{14} \end{aligned}$$

$$\therefore\ E(X) = (0 \times 0) + (1 \times \frac{1}{14}) + (2 \times \frac{4}{14}) + (3 \times \frac{9}{14})$$

$$= \frac{36}{14} = \frac{18}{7} = 2\frac{4}{7}$$

(b) For the continuous variable, we have:

$$f(x) = kx^2 \quad 0 \le x \le 3$$

$$\int_0^3 f(x)\,dx = 1 \text{ (since total probability must be 1)}$$

$$\int_0^3 kx^2\,dx = 1$$

$$k\left[\frac{1}{3}x^3\right]_0^3 = 1 \Rightarrow k = \frac{1}{9}$$

To find E(X), we evaluate $\int x\,f(x)\,dx$ over the interval for which f(x) is defined

$$E(X) = \int_0^3 x\frac{1}{9}x^2\,dx = \frac{1}{9}\int_0^3 x^3\,dx = \frac{1}{9}\left[\frac{1}{4}x^4\right]_0^3 = 2.25$$

Properties of expectation

The definitions for E(X) extend to $\mathrm{E}(\mathrm{g}(X))$ where g is a function of X and they are as follows:

For the discrete case with distribution as shown

x	x_1	x_2	...	x_n
$\mathrm{P}(X = x)$	p_1	p_2	...	p_n

$$\mathrm{E}(\mathrm{g}(x)) = \mathrm{g}(x_1)\, p_1 + \mathrm{g}(x_2)\, p_2 + \ldots + \mathrm{g}(x_n)\, p_n$$
$$= \sum_{i=1}^{n} \mathrm{g}(x_i)\, p_i$$

e.g. $\mathrm{E}(X^2) = x_1^{\,2}\, p_1 + x_2^{\,2}\, p_2 + \ldots + x_n^{\,2}\, p_n$

For the continuous case with PDF f(x) defined on the interval $[a, b]$

$$\mathrm{E}(\mathrm{g}(x)) = \int_a^b \mathrm{g}(x) \times \mathrm{f}(x)\, \mathrm{d}x$$

e.g. $$\mathrm{E}(X^2) = \int_a^b x^2\, \mathrm{f}(x)\, \mathrm{d}x$$

It can be seen that our earlier definitions of E(X) can be regarded as special cases of this general statement.

Example For the discrete distribution:

x	0	1	2	3	4
$\mathrm{P}(X = x)$	0.2	0.1	0.1	0.3	0.3

Find:

(a) E(X) (b) E(X^2) (c) E($5X$)

Solution

(a) $$\mathrm{E}(X) = \sum_{x=0}^{4} x\ \mathrm{P}(X = x)$$
$$= (0 \times 0.2) + (1 \times 0.1) + (2 \times 0.1) + (3 \times 0.3) + (4 \times 0.3)$$
$$= 2.4$$

(b) $$\mathrm{E}(X^2) = \sum_{x=0}^{4} x^2\, \mathrm{P}(X = x)$$
$$= (0^2 \times 0.2) + (1^2 \times 0.1) + (2^2 \times 0.1) + (3^2 \times 0.3) + (4^2 \times 0.3)$$
$$= 8.0$$

(c) $E(5X) = \sum_{x=0}^{4} 5x \; P(X = x)$

$= (5 \times 0 \times 0.2) + (5 \times 1 \times 0.1) + (5 \times 2 \times 0.1) + (5 \times 3 \times 0.3) + (5 \times 4 \times 0.3)$

$= 12.0$

And so $E(5X) = 5\,E(X)$

This result suggests a number of properties:

> If X is a random variable, either discrete or continuous, and a is a constant, then:
>
> (i) $E(a) = a$
>
> (ii) $E(aX + b) = aE(X) + b$
>
> (iii) $E\big(f_1(X) + f_2(X)\big) = E\big(f_1(X)\big) + E\big(f_2(X)\big)$
>
> where f_1 and f_2 are any two functions of X.

Example

A continuous random variable X has PDF given by:

$$f(x) = \begin{cases} 6x - 1 - 3x^2 & 0 \le x \le 1 \\ 0 & \text{elsewhere} \end{cases}$$

Find:

(a) $E(X)$

(b) $E(2X)$

(c) $E(X + 2)$

(d) $E(4X^2 - 2X)$

Solution

(a) $E(X) = \int_0^1 x\,(6x - 1 - 3x^2)\,dx = \int_0^1 (6x^2 - x - 3x^3)\,dx$

$= \left[\frac{6x^3}{3} - \frac{x^2}{2} - \frac{3x^4}{4}\right]_0^1 = \left(2 - \frac{1}{2} - \frac{3}{4}\right) - (0) = \frac{3}{4}$

(b) $E(2X) = 2E(X) = 2 \times \frac{3}{4} = 1\frac{1}{2}$

(c) $E(X + 2) = E(X) + E(2) = \frac{3}{4} + 2 = 2\frac{3}{4}$

(d) $E(4X^2 - 2X) = E(4X^2) - E(2X) = 4E(X^2) - 2E(X)$

To find this we need to find $E(X^2)$

$$E(X^2) = \int_0^1 x^2 (6x - 1 - 3x^2)\ dx$$

$$= \int_0^1 (6x^3 - x^2 - 3x^4)\ dx$$

$$= \left[\frac{6x^4}{4} - \frac{x^3}{3} - \frac{3x^5}{5} \right]_0^1$$

$$= \left(\frac{6}{4} - \frac{1}{3} - \frac{3}{5} \right) - (0) = \frac{17}{30} \approx 0.57$$

Hence $E(4X^2 - 2X) = 4 \times \frac{17}{30} - 2 \times \frac{3}{4} = \frac{23}{30} \approx 0.77$

The variance of X

The definitions of variance for discrete and continous random variables are analagous to the formulae for sample data which we met in Section 4. They are:

$$\text{Var}(X) = \sum_{i=1}^{n} (x_i - \mu)^2\ P(X = x_i)$$

$$\text{Var}(X) = \int_a^b (x - \mu)^2\ f(x)\ dx$$

respectively, where μ is written for $E(X)$.

Both formulae become:

$$\text{Var}(X) = E(X^2) - (E(X))^2$$

by some algebraic manipulation similar to that on pages 46–47 and in practice this is the formula to use in both cases.

As with the expected value, there are a number of useful properties.

If X is a random variable and a and b are two constants then:

(a) $\text{Var}(a) = 0$

(b) $\text{Var}(aX) = a^2\,\text{Var}(X)$

(c) $\text{Var}(aX + b) = a^2\,\text{Var}(X)$

It is worthwhile investigating these properties in more detail.

Proof of Property (a)

If a is some constant then we have:

$$\text{Var}(a) = \text{E}(a^2) - \text{E}(a)^2$$

which from the expectation properties we examined earlier implies that:

$$\text{Var}(a) = a^2 - a^2 = 0$$

Intuitively this appears reasonable. Given that the variance can be seen as a measure of dispersion, we know that the dispersion of a constant is zero.

Proof of Property (b)

$$\begin{aligned} \text{Var}(aX) &= \text{E}(a^2X^2) - \text{E}(aX)^2 \\ &= a^2\text{E}(X^2) - a^2\,\text{E}(X)^2 \end{aligned}$$

(from the expectation properties introduced earlier)

$$= a^2\,(\text{E}(X^2) - \text{E}(X)^2) = a^2\,\text{Var}(X)$$

Proof of Property (c)

$$\text{Var}(aX + b) = a^2\,\text{Var}(X)$$

This may seem somewhat surprising until we recollect the meaning of the variance. Effectively we are adding some constant, b, to a variable. This will affect the variable's location (its mean or expected value), but not its dispersion. So two distributions:

aX and $aX + b$

will have the same variance Var(aX)

Example

(a) Consider the following frequency distribution:

x	0	1	2	3	4
f	2	1	1	2	4

Find the mean and variance of this distribution using the formulae from Section 3 and 4.

(b) Now consider the probability distribution of the random variable X:

x	0	1	2	3	4
$P(X = x)$	0.2	0.1	0.1	0.2	0.4

where X is a model of the data above.

Find E(X) and Var(X) for this distribution.

Solution For part (a) the appropriate formulae are:

$$\bar{x} = \frac{\Sigma fx}{\Sigma f} = 2.5$$

$$s^2 = \frac{\Sigma fx^2}{\Sigma f} - \left[\frac{\Sigma fx}{\Sigma f}\right]^2 = 8.7 - 2.5^2 = 2.45$$

For part (b) we have:

$$\mathrm{E}(X) = \Sigma x\,\mathrm{P}(X = x) = 2.5$$

$$\begin{aligned}\mathrm{E}(X^2) &= \Sigma x^2\,\mathrm{P}(X = x)\\ &= 0^2 \times 0.2 + 1^2 \times 0.1 + 2^2 \times 0.1 + 3^2 \times 0.2 + 4^2 \times 0.4\\ &= 8.7\end{aligned}$$

$$\mathrm{Var}(X) = \mathrm{E}(X^2) - \mathrm{E}(X)^2 = 8.7 - 2.5^2 = 2.45$$

Example For the continuous random variable X with PDF

$$\mathrm{f}(x) = \begin{cases}\frac{1}{2}(x + 1) & -1 \le x \le 1\\ 0 & \text{otherwise}\end{cases}$$

Find:

(a) E(X) (b) Var(X)

Solution

(a) $$\mathrm{E}(X) = \int_{-1}^{1} x\,\frac{1}{2}(x + 1)\,\mathrm{d}x$$

$$= \frac{1}{2}\int_{-1}^{1}(x^2 + x)\,\mathrm{d}x = \frac{1}{2}\left[\frac{x^3}{3} + \frac{x^2}{2}\right]_{-1}^{1} = \frac{1}{3}$$

(b) $$\mathrm{Var}(X) = \mathrm{E}(X^2) - \mathrm{E}(X)^2 = \int_{-1}^{1} x^2\,\frac{1}{2}(x + 1)\,\mathrm{d}x - \left(\frac{1}{3}\right)^2$$

$$= \frac{1}{2}\int_{-1}^{1} x^2\,(x + 1)\,\mathrm{d}x - \frac{1}{9} = \frac{1}{2}\int_{-1}^{1}(x^3 + x^2)\,\mathrm{d}x - \frac{1}{9} = \frac{1}{2}\left[\frac{x^4}{4} + \frac{x^3}{3}\right]_{-1}^{1} - \frac{1}{9} = \frac{2}{9}$$

You should now be able to complete Exercises 8–11 on pages 107–108.

Mode and median for a continuous random variable

We have met the ideas of mode and median of data in Sections 2 and 3.

We define the mode(s) of a continuous random variable X as the value(s) of X where the PDF of X takes a maximum value (if such values exist).

The median of X is the 'middle' value. Therefore $P(X \leq \text{median}) = \frac{1}{2}$.

More precisely, if X is a random variable with PDF

$$\begin{cases} f(x) & a \leq x \leq b \\ 0 & \text{elsewhere} \end{cases}$$

then, by the usual calculus of turning points, any mode will be a local maximum of the probability curve and so will be found by solving $f'(x) = 0$ with $f''(x) < 0$. The median m is given by solving

$$\int_a^m f(x)\,dx = \frac{1}{2}$$

or equivalently:

$$F(x) = \frac{1}{2} \text{ if } F(x) \text{ is known.}$$

Example

A random variable X has PDF given by

$$f(x) = \begin{cases} cx(4-x)^2 & 0 \leq x \leq 4 \\ 0 & \text{otherwise} \end{cases}$$

(a) Find c.

(b) Give a sketch of the PDF of X.

(c) Find the mode of X.

Solution

(a) For $f(x)$ to be a PDF it must satisfy $\int_a^b f(x)\,dx = 1$

$$\Rightarrow \int_0^4 cx(4-x)^2\,dx = 1$$

$$\Rightarrow c\int_0^4 (16x - 8x^2 + x^3)\,dx = 1$$

$$\Rightarrow c\left[8x^2 - \frac{8x^3}{3} + \frac{x^4}{4}\right]_0^4 = 1 \Rightarrow c\left[128 - \frac{512}{3} + 64\right] = 1$$

$$\Rightarrow c = \frac{3}{64}$$

Hence $f(x) = \begin{cases} \frac{3}{64}x(4-x)^2 & 0 \leq x \leq 4 \\ 0 & \text{elsewhere} \end{cases}$ is the PDF of X

(b) It is often helpful to give a sketch of a PDF even if the question doesn't ask for it.

In this example the sketch is as in Figure 6.3.

Figure 6.3

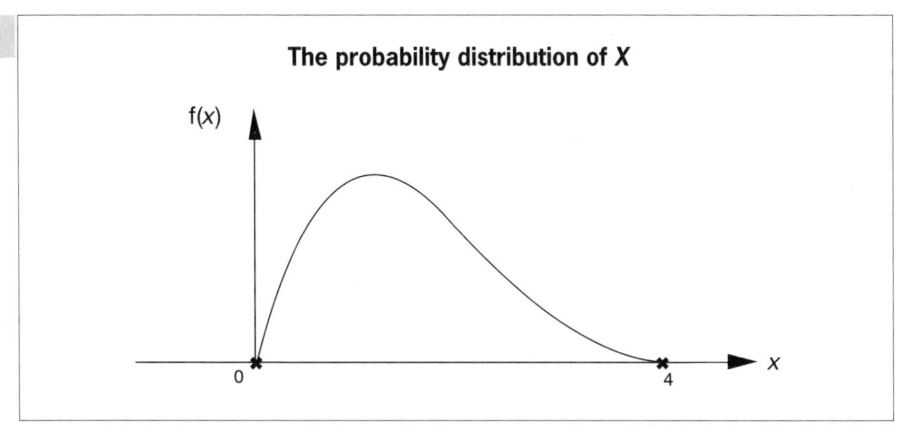

(c) The mode of X is formed from values of x where $f'(x) = 0$ and at which $f''(x) < 0$ in the interval $0 \leq x \leq 4$ (the condition $f''(x) < 0$ ensures a maximum point).

$$f(x) = \frac{3}{64}x(4-x)^2 = \frac{3x}{4} - \frac{3x^2}{8} + \frac{3x^3}{64}$$

$$\Rightarrow f'(x) = \frac{3}{4} - \frac{6x}{8} + \frac{9x^2}{64}$$

$$f'(x) = 0 \Rightarrow \frac{3}{4} - \frac{6x}{8} + \frac{9x^2}{64} = 0$$

$$\Rightarrow 9x^2 - 48x + 48 = 0$$

$$\Rightarrow 3x^2 - 16x + 16 = 0$$

$$\Rightarrow (3x-4)(x-4) = 0$$

$$\Rightarrow x = \frac{4}{3},\ x = 4$$

It should be obvious from our sketch that $x = \frac{4}{3}$ is the value required, but as a check we will work out $f''\left(\frac{4}{3}\right)$ and confirm that it is negative and that the point where $x = \frac{4}{3}$ is indeed the mode.

$$f''(x) = -\frac{6}{8} + \frac{18x}{64} = \frac{-3}{8} \text{ when } x = \frac{4}{3}.$$

so $x = \frac{4}{3}$ gives a maximum turning point and $x = \frac{4}{3}$ is the mode of $f(X)$.

Example The random variable X has PDF

$$f(x) = \frac{1}{72}x \qquad 0 \leq x \leq 12$$

Find the median of X.

Solution M, the median is given by:

$$\int_0^M \frac{1}{72}x\,dx = \tfrac{1}{2} \Rightarrow \left[\frac{x^2}{144}\right]_0^M = \tfrac{1}{2}$$

$$\Rightarrow \frac{M^2}{144} = \frac{1}{2}$$

$$\Rightarrow M^2 = 72$$

$$\Rightarrow M = \sqrt{72} \approx 8.49$$

(This result can easily be confirmed by considering the graph of f(x) and using areas of triangles which is left as an exercise for you.)

It was noted above that a sketch of the PDF can be valuable. If the resulting graph is symmetrical, then no further calculation of mean or median is required. They will both lie on the line of symmetry.

You should now be able to complete Exercise 12 on page 108.

Combinations of random variables

Finally in this section we investigate the properties of linear combinations of independent random variables. The results we establish will apply to both discrete and continuous random variables but we will work with the simpler of the two – namely discrete random variables.

Example Let X be defined by the distribution

x	0	1	2
$P(X = x)$	$\frac{1}{2}$	$\frac{1}{3}$	$\frac{1}{6}$

and let Y be defined by the distribution

y	–1	0	1
$P(Y = y)$	$\frac{1}{4}$	$\frac{1}{4}$	$\frac{1}{2}$

Then we can form many new distributions from these two. Probably the simplest are $Z = X + Y$ and $W = X - Y$.

We do this by first working out the possible outcomes for Z and then the respective probabilities for these outcomes.

Working systematically Z and W can take values:

X	Y	$Z = X + Y$	$W = X - Y$	Probability
0	–1	–1	1	$\frac{1}{2} \times \frac{1}{4}$
0	0	0	0	$\frac{1}{2} \times \frac{1}{4}$
0	1	1	–1	$\frac{1}{2} \times \frac{1}{2}$
1	–1	0	2	$\frac{1}{3} \times \frac{1}{4}$
1	0	1	1	$\frac{1}{3} \times \frac{1}{4}$
1	1	2	0	$\frac{1}{3} \times \frac{1}{2}$
2	–1	1	3	$\frac{1}{6} \times \frac{1}{4}$
2	0	2	2	$\frac{1}{6} \times \frac{1}{4}$
2	1	3	1	$\frac{1}{6} \times \frac{1}{2}$

We shall deal first with Z. Tidying up gives:

z	–1	0	1	2	3
$P(Z = z)$	$\frac{3}{24}$	$\frac{5}{24}$	$\frac{9}{24}$	$\frac{5}{24}$	$\frac{2}{24}$

where for example the probability for $Z = 0$ has been obtained by evaluating $\frac{1}{2} \times \frac{1}{4} + \frac{1}{3} \times \frac{1}{4}$.

Note that Z is a proper random variable since the probabilities add up to 1. It's always worth checking this.

Example Find E(X), E(Y), E(Z) from the previous example.

Solution

$$E(X) = 0 \times \frac{1}{2} + 1 \times \frac{1}{3} + 2 \times \frac{1}{6} = \frac{2}{3}$$

$$E(Y) = -1 \times \frac{1}{4} + 0 \times \frac{1}{4} + 1 \times \frac{1}{2} = \frac{1}{4}$$

$$E(Z) = -1 \times \frac{3}{24} + 0 \times \frac{5}{24} + 1 \times \frac{9}{24} + 2 \times \frac{5}{24} + 3 \times \frac{2}{24} = \frac{11}{12}$$

It can now be confirmed that $E(X + Y) = E(X) + E(Y)$

Example Find Var(X), Var(Y), Var(Z) from the same example.

Solution We need $E(X^2)$, $E(Y^2)$, $E(Z^2)$

$$E(X^2) = 0^2 \times \frac{1}{2} + 1^2 \times \frac{1}{3} + 2^2 \times \frac{1}{6} = 1$$

$$E(Y^2) = (-1)^2 \times \frac{1}{4} + 0^2 \times \frac{1}{4} + 1^2 \times \frac{1}{2} = \frac{3}{4}$$

$$E(Z^2) = (-1)^2 \times \frac{3}{24} + 0^2 \times \frac{5}{24} + 1^2 \times \frac{9}{24} + 2^2 \times \frac{5}{24} + 3^2 \times \frac{2}{24} = \frac{50}{24}$$

and therefore

$$\text{Var}(X) = 1 - \left(\frac{2}{3}\right)^2 = \frac{5}{9}$$

$$\text{Var}(Y) = \frac{3}{4} - \left(\frac{1}{4}\right)^2 = \frac{11}{16}$$

$$\text{Var}(Z) = \frac{50}{24} - \left(\frac{11}{12}\right)^2 = \frac{179}{144}$$

It can now be seen that Var(X) + Var(Y) = Var($X + Y$)

For W we have:

w	-1	0	1	2	3
$P(W = w)$	$\frac{6}{24}$	$\frac{7}{24}$	$\frac{7}{24}$	$\frac{3}{24}$	$\frac{1}{24}$

So $E(W) = \frac{1}{24}(-6 + 7 + 6 + 3) = \frac{10}{24} = \frac{5}{12}$

And $E(W^2) = \frac{1}{24}(6 + 7 + 12 + 9) = \frac{34}{24} = \frac{17}{12}$

Then $\text{Var}(W) = \frac{17}{12} - \left(\frac{5}{12}\right)^2 = \frac{179}{144}$

This too is equal to Var (X) + Var (Y), *not* Var (X) – Var (Y) as you might at first think.

The results observed in the previous example are not coincidence but are general to linear combinations of random variables.

The following properties are important.

If X and Y are random variables and a and b are any real numbers then:

$$E(aX + bY) = a\,E(X) + bE(Y)$$
$$E(aX - bY) = a\,E(X) - bE(Y)$$

and if X and Y are *independent* random variables and a and b are any real numbers then

$$\text{Var}(aX + bY) = a^2\,\text{Var}(X) + b^2\,\text{Var}(Y)$$
$$\text{Var}(aX - bY) = a^2\,\text{Var}(X) + b^2\,\text{Var}(Y)$$

The proofs of these properties are not expected at 'A' level, but the results are important and should be remembered. Note in particular the sign change in the last of these.

Example

For random variable X, you are given $\text{E}(X) = 6$, $\text{Var}(X) = 5$

and for random variable Y, $\text{E}(Y) = 8$, $\text{Var}(Y) = 10$

Find:

(a) $\text{E}(2X + 3Y)$

(b) $\text{Var}(2X + 3Y)$

(c) $\text{E}(3X - 4Y)$

(d) $\text{Var}(3X - 4Y)$

Solution

(a) $\text{E}(2X + 3Y) = 2\text{E}(X) + 3\text{E}(Y)$
$= 2 \times 6 + 3 \times 5 = 27$

(b) $\text{Var}(2X + 3Y) = 4\,\text{Var}(X) + 9\,\text{Var}(Y)$
$= 4 \times 5 + 9 \times 10 = 110$

(c) $\text{E}(3X - 4Y) = 3\text{E}(X) - 4\text{E}(Y)$
$= 3 \times 6 - 4 \times 8 = -14$

(d) $\text{Var}(3X - 4Y) = 9\,\text{Var}(X) + 16\,\text{Var}(Y)$
$= 9 \times 5 + 16 \times 10 = 205$

Note that in (d) the sign changes in the first line.

You should now be able to complete Exercises 13–15 on pages 108–109.

EXERCISES

1 X is the random variable 'The number of red balls selected when 3 balls are drawn at random' from a bag which contains 5 red, 4 blue and 1 white ball.

Work out the probability distribution of X and find $P(X > 1)$.

2 In a game of chance, 3 fair coins are tossed. The score, X, is defined as the number of heads showing. Find the probabilities of every possible value of X and hence show that X is a discrete random variable.

3 The random variable X has the distribution given by the table

r	1	2	3	4
$P(X = r)$	k	$\frac{k}{2}$	$\frac{l}{3}$	$\frac{l}{4}$

In addition it is known that:

$$P(X \le 2) = 2\,P(X > 2)$$

Find $P(X = 2)$

4 The random variable X has probability density function

$$f(x) = \begin{cases} 10cx^2 & 0 \le x < 0.6 \\ 9c(1-x) & 0.6 \le x \le 1.0 \\ 0 & \text{otherwise} \end{cases}$$

where c is a constant.

(a) Find the value of c and sketch the graph of the probability density function.

The mode of a random variable X is the value of x for which the probability density function is a maximum.

(b) Write down the mode of X.

(c) Find the probability that X is less than 0.4.

5 The continuous random variable X has probability density function

$$f(x) = \begin{cases} 0 & x \le 0 \\ 6kx(1-x) & 0 < x < 1 \\ \dfrac{k}{x^2} & x \ge 1 \end{cases}$$

Find k and $P\left(X > \frac{1}{2}\right)$

6 For the PDF in Exercise 5 above, find the CDF $F(x)$ and find:

(a) $F(\frac{1}{2})$ (b) $F(5)$

7 The length of life X, in years, of a new sort of television tube is modelled by the continuous distribution with cumulative distribution function:

$$F(x) = \begin{cases} 0 & x \leq 0 \\ \frac{6}{1000}(5x^2 - \frac{1}{3}x^3) & 0 < x < 10 \\ 1 & x \geq 10 \end{cases}$$

(a) Find, and sketch, the probability density function of X.

(b) A small hotel buys 8 television sets for its bedrooms. Find the probability that no tubes fail in the first two years.

(c) I buy a television set, and the tube is still working after two years. Given this information, find the probability that the tube will not fail during the next two years.

(d) Give two reasons why the distribution above is unlikely to be realistic as a model for the distribution of lifetimes of television tubes.

8 Find the expectation and variance of the PDF you have found in Exercise 2.

9 A discrete random variable X has a probability function given by:

$$\left.\begin{array}{l} p(x) = kx^2 \\ p(x) = 0 \end{array}\right\} \begin{array}{l} x = 1, 2, 3 \\ \text{otherwise} \end{array}$$

Find the value of:

(a) k (b) $E(X)$ (c) $Var(X)$.

10 The continuous random variable Y has a rectangular distribution:

$$f(y) = \begin{cases} \frac{1}{\pi} & -\frac{\pi}{2} \leq y \leq \frac{\pi}{2} \\ 0 & \text{otherwise} \end{cases}$$

(a) Find the mean of Y

(b) Find the variance of Y.

11 The continuous random variable X has PDF:

$$f(x) = \begin{cases} k(x^2 + 2x) & 1 \le x \le 2 \\ 0 & \text{otherwise} \end{cases}$$

(a) Find the value of k.

(b) Find the mean and variance of x.

12 The random variable X has PDF given by:

$$f(x) = \begin{cases} 0 & x < 0 \\ kx(2-x) & 0 \le x \le 2 \\ 0 & x > 2 \end{cases}$$

Find:

(a) k (b) the mode of X (c) the median of X.

13 X and Y are independent random variables such that:

$$E(X) = 20, \text{Var}(X) = 2, E(Y) = 24, \text{Var}(Y) = 3.$$

Evaluate the following:

(a) $E(5X + 7)$

(b) $\text{Var}(5X + 7)$

(c) $E(5X + 7Y)$

(d) $\text{Var}(5X + 7Y)$

(e) $E(5X - 7Y)$

(f) $\text{Var}(5X - 7Y)$

(g) $E(5 - 7Y)$

(h) $\text{Var}(5 - 7Y)$

14 A random variable R takes the integer value r with probability $p(r)$ where

$p(r) = kr^3 \quad r = 1, 2, 3, 4$

$p(r) = 0 \quad$ otherwise

Find:

(a) the value of k and display the distribution on graph paper

(b) the mean and variance of the distribution

(c) the mean and variance of $5R - 3$

15 Discrete random variables X and Y have distributions given in the tables below:

x	0	1	2
$P(X=x)$	$\frac{1}{3}$	$\frac{1}{2}$	$\frac{1}{6}$

y	-1	1
$P(Y=y)$	$\frac{3}{4}$	$\frac{1}{4}$

Find the distributions of:

(a) $3X$

(b) $2Y$

(c) $3X + 2Y$.

and find:

(d) $E(X)$, $Var(X)$

(e) $E(Y)$, $Var(Y)$

(f) $E(3X + 2Y)$, $Var(3X + 2Y)$

Verify the results that:

$$E(3X + 2Y) = 3E(X) + 2E(Y)$$

$$Var(3X + 2Y) = 9Var(X) + 4Var(Y)$$

SUMMARY

Now you have completed this section you should understand that:

- random variables are either discrete or continuous
- probability density and distribution functions allow us to determine the probability of some event occurring for a defined random variable
- expected values are readily calculated for both types of random variable
- E(X) and Var (X) are the direct counterparts in probability distributions of the mean and variance of a frequency distribution.
- There are rules for expectation and variance of multiples and combinations of random variables.

SECTION

7

Discrete probability distributions

INTRODUCTION

In the last section we examined the nature of random variables. One of the aspects we investigated was the probability distribution of such variables. In statistics there are certain types of such distributions which are important enough to warrant specific investigation and analysis. In this section we introduce some of these special discrete distributions. In the next section we introduce the special continuous probability distributions. You should be familiar with the binomial series before starting this section.

The uniform distribution

The first distribution we examine is one of the simplest: the uniform. Simply, a random variable follows a **discrete uniform distribution** if X is discrete and each value of X has the same probability of occurring. More formally we can state that:

$$P(X = x_i) = \frac{1}{n} \quad x = x_1, x_2 \ldots x_n$$

$$= 0 \quad \text{otherwise}$$

A simple example of such a distribution would relate to the throwing of a six-sided die. Each side (each number from 1 to 6) has the same probability of appearing, that is, $\frac{1}{6}$. Using the principles developed in the last section we can also readily calculate the mean and variance of such a distribution.

Example

A bank clerk has noted that at a particular period during the day he can deal with between two and six customers in a given ten-minute period (the exact number of course will depend on what each customer wants to do). He has also noted that the number of customers dealt with follows a uniform distribution.

(a) Calculate the probability that in a ten-minute period the clerk will deal with at least five customers.

(b) Calculate the mean and variance of the distribution.

Solution We have a uniform distribution such that:

Number of customers, x	2	3	4	5	6
$P(X = x)$	0.2	0.2	0.2	0.2	0.2

For part (a), at least five customers implies five or six customers, with a probability:

$$P(5 \text{ or } 6 \text{ customers}) = 0.2 + 0.2 = 0.4$$

(b) The mean of the distribution is calculated from the appropriate formula:

$$E(X)= \Sigma\, xP(X = x) = (2 \times 0.2)+(3 \times 0.2)+(4 \times 0.2)+(5 \times 0.2)+(6 \times 0.2) = 4$$

That is, on average four customers will be dealt with by the clerk (hardly a surprising result given the symmetrical distribution).

The variance is given by:

$$\begin{aligned} \text{Var}(X) &= E(X^2) - E(X)^2 = \Sigma\, x^2 P(X = x) - 4^2 \\ &= 18 - 16 = 2 \end{aligned}$$

The binomial distribution

The second of our discrete probability distributions is one of the most important: the **binomial distribution**. We shall illustrate its important principles with a simple example.

Let us assume there is a small factory producing some particular item. In order to monitor the quality of the output produced in the factory an inspector is employed to regularly check the items. This is done by taking a small sample and seeing how many can be classed as faulty or as not faulty. On average 10% of items checked are found to be faulty.

The inspector chooses four items at random from the production line and wants to calculate the following probabilities:

P (0 items are faulty)

P (1 item is faulty)

P (2 items are faulty)

P (3 items are faulty)

P (4 items are faulty)

i.e. he wants to know the distribution of X – the number of faulty items in a sample of 4.

As we shall see this is typical of a problem where the binomial distribution is appropriate. Before proceeding we shall introduce the appropriate terminology.

A binomial situation can be recognised where:

1. an experiment consists of a number (n) of repetitive actions called trials
2. each trial has two mutually exclusive outcomes (generally referred to as success and failure)
3. the probability of success for each trial is denoted as p and remains constant
4. the trials are independent
5. we define the random variable X as the number of successes from the n trials.

Clearly for our example, $n = 4$. Success is defined as choosing a faulty item, so $p = 0.1$.

If X is a discrete random variable having a binomial distribution with number of independent trials = n and probability of success at each trial = p then we write:

$$X \sim \mathrm{B}(n, p)$$

where the symbol ~ is read as 'has the distribution'.

and B stands for 'binomial'.

n and p are called the *parameters of the distribution.*

In our example, X is the number of faulty items in a sample of 4 where each item has a probability of $p = 0.1$ of being faulty

so $X \sim \mathrm{B}(4, 0.1)$

We now proceed to work out the probability distribution for this random variable.

P(X = 0)

$X = 0$ means that no items are faulty and since each item is not faulty with probability 0.9 independently of the other

$$\mathrm{P}(X = 0) = (0.9) \times (0.9) \times (0.9) \times (0.9) = (0.9)^4.$$

P(X = 1)

$X = 1$ means one faulty item and therefore three non-faulty items.

The ways in which this can occur are

$$\mathrm{F}\bar{\mathrm{F}}\bar{\mathrm{F}}\bar{\mathrm{F}} \text{ or } \bar{\mathrm{F}}\mathrm{F}\bar{\mathrm{F}}\bar{\mathrm{F}} \text{ or } \bar{\mathrm{F}}\bar{\mathrm{F}}\mathrm{F}\bar{\mathrm{F}} \text{ or } \bar{\mathrm{F}}\bar{\mathrm{F}}\bar{\mathrm{F}}\mathrm{F}$$

where F indicates faulty and $\overline{\text{F}}$ indicates not faulty

Hence $P(X = 1) = 4 \times (0.9)^3 \times (0.1)$

P(X = 2)

$X = 2$ means 2 faulty and 2 non-faulty, and proceeding as before we get:

$$\overline{\text{F}}\overline{\text{F}}\text{FF} \text{ or } \overline{\text{F}}\text{F}\overline{\text{F}}\text{F} \text{ or } \overline{\text{F}}\text{FF}\overline{\text{F}} \text{ or } \text{F}\overline{\text{F}}\overline{\text{F}}\text{F} \text{ or } \text{F}\overline{\text{F}}\text{F}\overline{\text{F}} \text{ or } \text{FF}\overline{\text{F}}\overline{\text{F}}$$

giving $P(X = 2) = 6 \times (0.9)^2 \times (0.1)^2$

By now a pattern is emerging and the distribution is

x	0	1	2	3	4
$P(X = x)$	$(0.9)^4$	$4(0.9)^3\,(0.1)$	$6(0.9)^2\,(0.1)^2$	$4(0.9)\,(0.1)^3$	$(0.1)^4$

The remaining probabilities have been calculated using the pattern established by the first 3 calculations.

This example is representative of all binomial probability distributions and the pattern that is observed in the above table is always present.

The numbers which appear as 'coefficients' are numbers from Pascal's triangle (see Module P2, Section 10) – the 5th row in this particular example – and for small n can be obtained most easily using the triangle.

For large n, though, it is more sensible to use the fact that the numbers in Pascal's triangle are precisely the numbers $\binom{n}{r}$ or ${}^nC_r$, the number of combinations of r things out of n things. $\left[\text{Note } \binom{n}{r} = \frac{n!}{r!(n-r)!}\right]$

In fact for $X \sim B(n, p)$ there is a formula for $P(X = r)$ namely

$$P(X = r) = \binom{n}{r} p^r (1-p)^{n-r}$$

which is made up of the product of

$\binom{n}{r}$	the coefficient representing the number of ways in which r successes can occur in n trials.
p^r	representing the r successes occurring with probability p each
$(1-p)^{n-r}$	representing the $n - r$ failures occurring with probability $1 - p$ each.

Example

$X \sim B(3, 0.4)$ i.e. X is a discrete random variable having a binomial distribution with parameters n (the number of trials) = 3 and p (the probability of success at any trial) = 0.4

Write out the probability distribution of X and find $E(X)$ and $Var(X)$

Solution

Note first that the possible outcomes for B(3, 0.4) are 0, 1, 2, 3

i.e. we can have any number of successes from 0 to 3.

(This is true in general. For $B(n, p)$ the possible outcomes will be $0, 1, 2, \ldots, n$)

Note secondly that since 'success' occurs with probability 0.4, 'failure' occurs with probability 0.6, since success and failure are mutually exclusive.

The probability distribution using techniques employed previously will be:

x	0	1	2	3
$P(X = x)$	$(0.6)^3$	$3(0.6)^2\,(0.4)$	$3(0.6)^3\,(0.4)^2$	$(0.4)^3$

where for example the coefficient for $x = 1$ is obtained by $\binom{3}{1}$ for the number of ways of obtaining one success in 3 trials.

The probabilities work out to the following as fractions:

x	0	1	2	3
$P(X = x)$	$\frac{216}{1000}$	$\frac{432}{1000}$	$\frac{288}{1000}$	$\frac{64}{1000}$

from which it can be readily seen that the probabilities add up to 1.

In this form it is a simple matter to calculate $E(X)$ and $E(X^2)$.

$$E(X) = 0 \times \frac{216}{1000} + 1 \times \frac{432}{1000} + 2 \times \frac{288}{1000} + 3 \times \frac{64}{1000}$$

$$= \frac{1200}{1000} = 1.2$$

$$E(X^2) = 0^2 \times \frac{216}{1000} + 1^2 \times \frac{432}{1000} + 2^2 \times \frac{288}{1000} + 3^2 \times \frac{64}{1000}$$

$$= \frac{2160}{1000} = 2.16$$

$$\Rightarrow \text{Var}(X) = E(X^2) - (E(X))^2$$

$$= 2.16 - (1.2)^2 = 0.72$$

Now it turns out that

$$E(X) = 3 \times 0.4$$

$$\text{Var}(X) = 3 \times 0.4 \times 0.6$$

and this is not a coincidence.

In general for $X \sim B(n, p)$, $E(X) = np$

$$\text{Var}(X) = np(1-p)$$
$$= npq, \text{ where } q \text{ is often used for } 1-p$$

The proofs of these results in the general case are not part of the syllabus but you should be familiar with the results.

To summarise: If $X \sim B(n, p)$ i.e. X has a binomial distribution with number of trials = n and probability of success = p then:

$$P(X = r) = \binom{n}{r} p^r (1-p)^{n-r}$$

$E(X) = np$ $\qquad$ $\text{Var}(X) = np(1-p)$

Example

10% of items checked on a production line are found to be faulty. If we select ten items from the production line, find the chance that

(a) 3 items are faulty

(b) 4 or more items are faulty

(c) less than 3 items are faulty

(d) 7 or more items are non-faulty

Solution

Let X = number of items out of 10 which are faulty. Then $X \sim B(10, 0.1)$

(a) $$P(X = 3) = \binom{10}{3}(0.1)^3 (0.9)^7$$
$$= \frac{10!}{3!7!}(0.1)^3(0.9)^7$$
$$= 0.0574 \text{ (from calculator)}$$

(b) $P(X \geq 4)$ requires working out seven probabilities

A simpler approach is to find $P(X \leq 3)$ and subtract from 1, i.e. use the *complementary* event

$$P(X \leq 3) = P(X = 0) + P(X = 1) + P(X = 2) + P(X = 3)$$
$$= (0.9)^{10} + \binom{10}{1}(0.9)^9(0.1) + \binom{10}{2}(0.9)^8(0.1)^2 + \binom{10}{3}(0.9)^7(0.1)^3$$
$$= 0.3487 + 0.3874 + 0.1937 + 0.0574$$
$$= 0.987 \text{ (3 d.p.)}$$

$$\Rightarrow \quad P(X \geq 4) = 1 - 0.987 = 0.013 \quad (3 \text{ d.p.})$$

(c) $P(X < 3) = P(X = 0) + P(X = 1) + P(X = 2)$

$$= (0.9)^{10} + \frac{10!}{9!}(0.9)^9(0.1) + \frac{10!}{2!8!}(0.9)^8(0.1)^2$$

$$= 0.9298$$

(d) P (7 or 8 or 9 or 10 are good)

$= \text{P (3 or 2 or 1 or 0 are faulty)} = P(X \leq 3)$

$= 0.9872$ (as in (b))

Example

The office of a large company has recently bought a consignment of ten of the latest photocopying machines for use around the company. The office manager knows from previous experience that there is a 20% chance that any one machine will develop a fault within the first twelve months. The cost of repairing such a fault will be, on average, £125.

(a) What is the probability that at least eight of the machines will not break down in the first year?

(b) What is the probability that at least one machine will break down?

(c) How much money should be allocated over the next year to the repair budget for these machines?

Solution

(a) P (8 or 9 or 10 are OK)

$= \text{P (2 or 1 or 0 faulty)}$

$$= \frac{10!}{2!8!}(0.2)^2(0.8)^8 + \frac{10!}{9!}(0.2)(0.8)^9 + (0.8)^{10}$$

$$= 0.678$$

(b) P (at least one fault)

$= \text{P (1 or 2 or 3 or} \ldots \text{ or 10 faults)}$

$= 1 - \text{P (0 faults)}$

$= 1 - (0.8)^{10} = 0.893$

(c) For $n = 10, p = 0.2,$

Mean $= np = 10 \times 0.2 = 2$

$\therefore$ We expect 2 to break down

$\therefore$ We should budget for the sum $2 \times 125 = £250$.

You should now be able to complete Exercises 1–6 on page 123.

The Poisson distribution

The next of our probability distributions is the Poisson (pronounced 'Pwasonn') distribution. We shall see that it has similarities to the binomial and, indeed, in certain circumstances can be used to approximate the binomial distribution.

To illustrate the principles, let us use a simple example. The editor of this book has been checking the accuracy of the proofs before publication. It has been found that on average there are two minor misprints per page. We wish to determine the probability that on a given page there are:

(a) no misprints
(b) four or more misprints.

At first sight it does not appear obvious how we can proceed, based on the information given. There is no apparent way of determining such a probability. Clearly if we knew the number of words per page we could calculate the probability of a page containing a misprint, but this is information we are not given. It is in this type of situation that the Poisson distribution can be applied.

The Poisson distribution is a good model in a wide range of situations, the general theme of which is that of random (i.e. unpredictable) events happening in time or space. Further examples are:

X = the number of calls per 5 minute period coming into a telephone switchboard (random in time)

Y = the number of accidents occurring in a factory per week (random in time)

Z = the number of flaws per m^2 in a length of material produced in a factory (random in space)

In each of these situations the following requirements are met:

(a) Events occur randomly and one at a time.
(b) Events are independent of each other.
(c) The average number of events per interval is proportional to the length of the interval.

So, for example, in the example of the factory, if W is the number of accidents occurring in a fortnight then $E(W) = 2E(Y)$ simply because the time interval is twice as long.

The probabilities for a Poisson distribution are calculated from the formula:

$$P(X = r) = \frac{e^{-\mu}\mu^r}{r!} \quad r = 0, 1, 2 \ldots$$

where μ is the average number of occurrences (per unit time or area).

This is an example of a discrete random variable having an infinite number of possible outcomes.

In the example of the misprints per page at the beginning of this section, the average is 2 per page, so μ is 2 and the probability distribution will have the form:

r	0	1	2	3	4 ...
P($X = r$)	e^{-2}	$2e^{-2}$	$\frac{4e^{-2}}{2!}$	$\frac{8e^{-2}}{3!}$	$\frac{16e^{-2}}{4!}$

using the formula above (note that 0! = 1) and evaluation of these probabilities gives (to 3 d.p.):

r	0	1	2	3	4 ...
P($X = r$)	0.135	0.271	0.271	0.180	0.090 ...

It should be noticed that the probabilities rapidly become very small and in fact for the distribution given by adding the above probabilities $P(X \leq 4) = 0.947$ (3 d.p.). This means that $P(X \geq 5) = 0.053$. In practice of course the number of misprints per page will be a finite number.

The Poisson distribution which models this type of phenomenon can in theory take any whole number value ≥ 0, but, as we have seen above, large outcomes have very small (negligible) probabilities.

This obvious discrepancy between the reality of the situation being modelled and the probability distribution being used for the modelling does not invalidate the model however. The Poisson distribution provides a successful model for a diverse range of data arising from a wide variety of sources. It is instructive to check that the distribution has the basic property (i.e. the probabilities add up to 1).

Example Show that the Poisson distribution with mean μ is a proper probability distribution.

Solution If X is a Poisson distribution with mean μ we write $X \sim P(\mu)$ and the distribution is:

r	0	1	2	3 ...
P($X = r$)	$e^{-\mu}$	$\mu e^{-\mu}$	$\frac{\mu^2 e^{-\mu}}{2!}$	$\frac{\mu^3 e^{-\mu}}{3!}$ ...

$$\Sigma p_i = e^{-\mu} + \mu e^{-\mu} + \frac{\mu^2 e^{-\mu}}{2!} + \frac{\mu^3 e^{-\mu}}{3!} + \ldots$$

$$= e^{-\mu}\left[1 + \mu + \frac{\mu^2}{2!} + \frac{\mu^3}{3!} + \ldots\right] = e^{-\mu} \times e^{\mu} = 1$$

At the third line of the proof it was necessary to recognise that in brackets we had the expansion of e^{μ}.

Example For the problem given at the beginning of this section about the number of misprints per page, find the probability of 4 or more misprints per page.

Solution

$X \sim P(2)$

$$P(X \geq 4) = P\text{ (4 or 5 or 6 or ... misprints)}$$
$$= 1 - P\text{ (0 or 1 or 2 or 3 misprints)}$$
$$= 1 - \left[\frac{e^{-2}2^0}{0!} + \frac{e^{-2}2^1}{1!} + \frac{e^{-2}2^2}{2!} + \frac{e^{-2}2^3}{3!}\right]$$

Now take out a factor of e^{-2} and get:

$$= 1 - e^{-2}\left[1 + \frac{2}{1!} + \frac{2^2}{2!} + \frac{2^3}{3!}\right]$$

Now use your calculator and get:

$$= 1 - e^{-2}(6.333) = 1 - 0.8571 = 0.143 \quad \text{(3 d.p.)}$$

Example I expect to receive 3 letters a week. Use the Poisson distribution to find the chance of receiving:

(a) one letter this week

(b) at least three letters this week

(c) five letters during the next fortnight.

Solution If X = the number of letters received each week then $X \sim P(3)$.

(a) $P(X = 1) = \dfrac{e^{-3}3^1}{1!} = 0.149$ (3 d.p.)

(b) $P(X \geq 3)$

$$= P\text{ (3 or 4 or 5 or ... letters)}$$
$$= 1 - P\text{ (0 or 1 or 2 letters)}$$
$$= 1 - \left[\frac{e^{-3}3^0}{0!} + \frac{e^{-3}3^1}{1!} + \frac{e^{-3}3^2}{2!}\right]$$
$$= 1 - e^{-3}\left[1 + \frac{3}{1!} + \frac{3^2}{2!}\right] = 0.577 \quad \text{(3 d.p.)}$$

(c) If Y = the number of letters received in a fortnight then $Y \sim P(6)$

$$P(Y = 5) = \frac{e^{-6}6^5}{5!} = 0.161 \text{ (3 d.p.)}$$

The mean and variance of the Poisson distribution

The following derivations are unlikely to appear in your exam, but are included for completeness. We have stated that if $X \sim \mathrm{P}(\mu)$ then μ represents the average number of occurrences per unit interval and we now prove that this is in fact the case, i.e. $\mathrm{E}(X) = \mu$.

Recall that the distribution has the form:

r	0	1	2	3	4 ...
$\mathrm{P}(X = r)$	$e^{-\mu}$	$\mu e^{-\mu}$	$\frac{\mu^2 e^{-\mu}}{2!}$	$\frac{\mu^3 e^{-\mu}}{3!}$	$\frac{\mu^4 e^{-\mu}}{4!}$ ...

Hence:

$$\mathrm{E}(X) = 0 \times e^{-\mu} + 1 \times \mu e^{-\mu} + 2 \times \frac{\mu^2 e^{-\mu}}{2!} + 3 \times \frac{\mu^3 e^{-\mu}}{3!} + 4 \times \frac{\mu^4 e^{-\mu}}{4!} + \dots$$

$$\Rightarrow \mathrm{E}(X) = \mu e^{-\mu} + \mu^2 e^{-\mu} + \frac{\mu^3 e^{-\mu}}{2!} + \frac{\mu^4 e^{-\mu}}{3!} + \dots \text{ (by cancelling)}$$

$$\Rightarrow \mathrm{E}(X) = \mu e^{-\mu}\left(1 + \mu + \frac{\mu^2}{2!} + \frac{\mu^3}{3!} + \dots\right)$$

$$\Rightarrow \mathrm{E}(X) = \mu e^{-\mu} e^{\mu} \text{ (by recognising } e^{\mu} \text{ in the brackets)}$$

$$\Rightarrow \mathrm{E}(X) = \mu$$

In order to obtain the variance we need to first find $\mathrm{E}(X^2)$

$$\mathrm{E}(X^2) = 0^2 \times e^{-\mu} + 1^2 \times \mu e^{-\mu} + 2^2 \times \frac{\mu^2 e^{-\mu}}{2!} + 3^2 \times \frac{\mu^3 e^{-\mu}}{3!} + 4^2 \times \frac{\mu^4 e^{-\mu}}{4!} + \dots$$

$$= \mu e^{-\mu} + 2\mu^2 e^{-\mu} + \frac{3\mu^3 e^{-\mu}}{2!} + \frac{4\mu^4 e^{-\mu}}{3!} + \dots$$

$$= \mu e^{-\mu}\left[1 + 2\mu + \frac{3\mu^2}{2!} + \frac{4\mu^3}{3!} + \dots\right]$$

$$= \mu e^{-\mu}\left[1 + (\mu + \mu) + \left(\frac{\mu^2}{2!} + \frac{2\mu^2}{2!}\right) + \left(\frac{\mu^3}{3!} + \frac{3\mu^3}{3!}\right) + \dots\right]$$

$$= \mu e^{-\mu}\left[\left(1 + \mu + \frac{\mu^2}{2!} + \frac{\mu^3}{3!} + \dots\right) + \left(\mu + \mu^2 + \frac{\mu^3}{2!} + \dots\right)\right]$$

$$= \mu e^{-\mu}\left[e^{\mu} + \mu\left(1 + \mu + \frac{\mu^2}{2!} + \dots\right)\right]$$

$$= \mu e^{-\mu}\left[e^{\mu} + \mu e^{\mu}\right]$$

$$= \mu + \mu^2$$

Hence $\mathrm{Var}(X) = \mu + \mu^2 - \mu^2$

$$\Rightarrow \mathrm{Var}(X) = \mu$$

This is an interesting result about the Poisson distribution. If $X \sim \mathrm{P}(\mu)$ then

$$\mathrm{E}(X) = \mu \qquad \mathrm{Var}(X) = \mu$$

If we have some discrete data and there is some evidence that it comes from a Poisson distribution, then further supporting evidence for this belief will be obtained by checking to see if the mean and variance have similar values. If they are found to be very different, then these would be good grounds for believing that the data comes from a distribution other than the Poisson.

In summary: If X is a discrete random variable having a Poisson distribution with average frequency μ per time or space interval, we write

$$X \sim \mathrm{P}(\mu)$$

and probabilities can be calculated from the formula:

$$\mathrm{P}(X = r) = \frac{\mu^r e^{-\mu}}{r!} \qquad r = 0, 1, 2, \ldots$$

and $\mathrm{E}(X) = \mu$

$\mathrm{Var}(X) = \mu$

You should now be able to attempt Exercises 7–8 on page 124.

Poisson approximation to the binomial

The Poisson distribution is one with wide application in its own right, but its origin lies in an attempt by the French mathematician Poisson (1781–1840) to obtain binomial probabilities for large n. The derivation is difficult and not examinable, but the result is very useful and should be known.

If $X \sim \mathrm{B}(n, p)$ where p is small and n is large

then the binomial probabilities can be well approximated by the Poisson distribution having the same mean.

i.e. $X \sim \mathrm{B}(n, p) \Rightarrow X \approx \mathrm{P}(n \times p)$

where $\approx$ is taken to mean 'is approximately distributed'.

Generally good approximations are obtained for $n > 50$ and $p < 0.1$.

Example

Return to our binomial example where we were sampling production to check the probability of a given number of faulty items being found. Assume that we now take samples of 100 items. Then the number of faulty items is $X \sim \mathrm{B}(100, 0.1)$

Using the binomial formula calculate the chance of 8 faulty items.

Solution

$$P\text{ (8 faults)} = \frac{100!}{8!\,92!}(0.1)^8(0.9)^{92}$$

Now we have a problem because most calculators cannot cope with 100!

We *could* proceed as follows:

$$P\text{ (8 faults)} = \frac{100\times 99\times 98\times 97\times 96\times 95\times 94\times 93}{1\times 2\times 3\times 4\times 5\times 6\times 7\times 8}(0.1)^8(0.9)^{92}$$

$$= 0.1148\ \text{(4 d.p.)}$$

However, with n large and p small we can use the Poisson approximation.

Using the Poisson formula determine this probability approximately. For the Poisson distribution we have $\mu = np = 10$

And so:

$$X \sim P(10)$$

$$P(X = 8) = \frac{e^{-10}\,10^8}{8!} = 0.113$$

And so the Poisson approximation in this case is accurate to 2 places of decimals.

Example

In a certain draw, each ticket has a probability of 0.02 of winning a prize. Kevin has 100 tickets for the draw. Find, using the Poisson approximation, the probability that he wins more than 3 prizes.

Solution

If X is the number of prizes he wins then

$$X \sim B(100, 0.02)$$

(The actual distribution is binomial since for each of his 100 tickets there is a final probability of 0.02 of winning.)

$$\Rightarrow X \approx P(2)$$

$$P(X > 3) = P(X = 4) + P(X = 5) + \ldots$$

$$= 1 - P(X = 0) - P(X = 1) - P(X = 2) - P(X = 3)$$

$$= 1 - \left(e^{-2} + 2e^{-2} + \frac{2^2e^{-2}}{2!} + \frac{2^3e^{-2}}{3!}\right)$$

$$= 1 - e^{-2}\left(1 + 2 + 2 + \frac{4}{3}\right)$$

$$= 1 - e^{-2}\left(\frac{19}{3}\right) = 0.143$$

It is worth noting that tables of binomial and Poisson cumulative probabilities are available for use with larger values of n, where calculation would be too time-consuming. (Copies of these tables are included as Appendices 3 and 4.) The tables are quite simple to use and you can quickly become familiar with them by practising a few examples.

You should now be able to complete Exercises 9–11 on page 124–125.

EXERCISES

1 Random variable X has the discrete uniform distribution with outcomes 1, 2, ..., n. Using the results

$$1 + 2 + \ldots + n = \frac{1}{2}n\,(n + 1)$$

and $$1^2 + 2^2 + \ldots + n^2 = \frac{1}{6}n\,(n + 1)\,(2n + 1)$$

find E(X), Var (X) and P($X > m$) simplifying your answers as much as possible.

2 Random variable X is 'the number of bad eggs in a batch of 10 eggs' where for each egg there is a probability of 0.15 of it being bad. State the distribution of X and find P($X \geq 4$), P($X >$ E(X)).

3 A school decides to have its fire drill in a particular week. They program a computer to decide when the drill will be held (!). The computer chooses days at random with a probability of $p = 0.35$ of choosing any particular day. No one thought to tell the computer to choose only one day. Let X be the number of fire drills held in that 5-day week.

(a) Calculate the PDF of X and state its mean and variance.

(b) What value of p should they choose to give an expected value of one fire drill during the week? What would be the probability of more than one fire drill?

4 A certain person can hit the bullseye on a dartboard with probability 0.4. How many throws must he make to have a probability of at least 0.9 of hitting the bullseye at least once?

5 If $X \sim B(10, 0.2)$, use cumulative binomial tables (Appendix 3) to find:

(a) P($X \leq 3$) (b) P($X > 6$) (c) P($4 \leq X < 8$)

6 If $X \sim B\,(10, 0.8)$, use the tables to find $P(X \leq 3)$.

7 A shop sells a particular make of radio at a rate of 4 per week on average. The number sold in a week is thought to have a Poisson distribution.

(a) Using a Poisson distribution, find the probability that the shop sells at least 2 in a week.

(b) Find the smallest number that can be in stock at the beginning of a week in order to have at least a 99% chance of being able to meet all demands during that week.

(c) Comment on the applicability of a Poisson distribution.

8 The number of accidents per week at a certain intersection has a Poisson distribution with parameter 2.5. Find the probability that

(a) exactly 5 accidents will occur in a week,

(b) more than 14 accidents will occur in 4 weeks.

9 $X \sim B(35, 0.1)$. Use the Poisson approximation to the Binomial to find $P(X \leq 5)$.

10 (a) The probability distribution of a discrete random variable, X, is defined by

$$P(X = x) = \begin{cases} e^{-\lambda} \dfrac{\lambda^x}{x!} & \text{for } x = 0, 1, 2, \ldots\ldots, (\lambda > 0) \\ 0 & \text{otherwise} \end{cases}$$

Derive the mean and variance of X.

(b) A shopkeeper hires vacuum cleaners to the general public at £5 per day. The mean daily demand is 2.6.

(i) Calculate the expected daily income from this activity assuming an unlimited number of vacuum cleaners is available.

The demand follows a Poisson distribution.

(ii) Find the probability that the demand on a particular day is (a) 0, (b) exactly one, (c) exactly two, (d) three or more.

(iii) If only 3 vacuum cleaners are available for hire calculate the mean of the daily income.

A nearby large store is willing to lend vacuum cleaners at short notice to the shopkeeper, so that in practice she will always be able to meet any demand. The store would charge £2 per day for this service regardless of how many, if any, cleaners are actually borrowed.

Would you advise the shopkeeper to take up this offer? Explain your answer.

[AEB 1992]

11 If $X \sim P(3.5)$, use tables to find:
(a) $P(X \leq 10)$ (b) $P(X \geq 8)$ (c) $P(5 \leq X \leq 11)$

SUMMARY

Now that you have completed this section, you should understand that:

- the uniform distribution is appropriate where events have an equal probability of occurring
- the binomial distribution is applied to conditions where only 'success' or 'failure' are possible
- the Poisson distribution can be applied to situations where we only know the average value of some discrete event in time or space
- Binomial probabilities can be approximated by the Poisson distribution for large *n* and small *p*.

SECTION

Continuous probability distributions

INTRODUCTION

In the last section we introduced a number of discrete probability distributions. In this section we extend our analysis to examine two continuous probability distributions.

By the end of this section you will be able to:

- use the continuous uniform distribution
- use the normal distribution
- understand and use the standardised normal distribution
- approximate the binomial and Poisson distributions using the normal.

The continuous uniform distribution

In Section 7 we met the discrete uniform distribution where each outcome had the same probability. The continuous uniform distribution is defined as follows:

> Random variable X has a distribution which is uniform in the interval $a \le x \le b$ if:
>
> $$f(x) = \begin{cases} \dfrac{1}{b-a} & \text{for } a \le x \le b \\ 0 & \text{otherwise} \end{cases}$$

We write $X \sim U(a, b)$ if X is a random variable with a continuous uniform distribution.

The PDF of X is shown in Figure 8.1

Figure 8.1

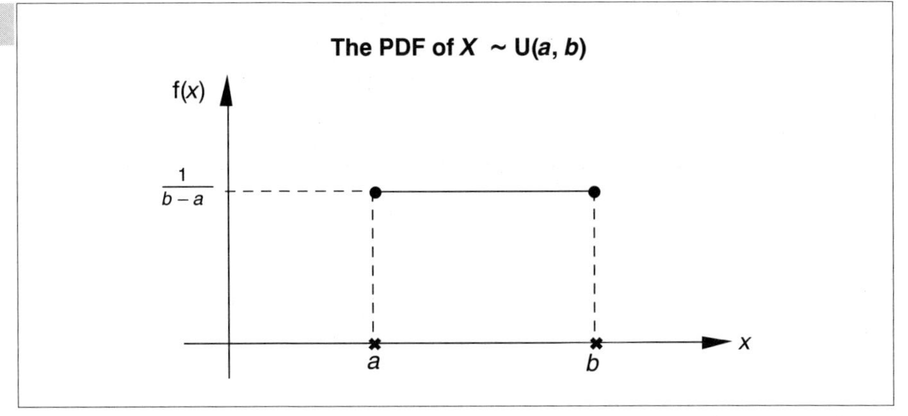

Note that the basic requirement for a PDF is satisfied since the area under the 'curve' is:

$$(b-a) \times \frac{1}{(b-a)} = 1$$

Mean and variance of X ~ U(a, b)

The mean and variance of the distribution are very easily calculated:

$$\text{E}(X) = a + \frac{b-a}{2} = \frac{a+b}{2}$$

(by symmetry from Figure 8.1)

$$\text{E}(X^2) = \int_a^b x^2 \left(\frac{1}{b-a}\right) \text{d}x$$

$$= \frac{1}{b-a} \int_a^b x^2 \,\text{d}x$$

$$= \frac{1}{b-a} \left[\frac{x^3}{3}\right]_a^b$$

$$= \frac{1}{b-a} \left(\frac{b^3}{3} - \frac{a^3}{3}\right)$$

$$= \left(\frac{1}{b-a}\right)\left(\frac{b^3 - a^3}{3}\right)$$

$$= \left(\frac{1}{b-a}\right)\left(\frac{(b-a)\,(b^2 + ab + a^2)}{3}\right)$$

$$= \frac{b^2 + ab + a^2}{3}$$

$$\text{So Var}(X) = \frac{b^2 + ab + a^2}{3} - \left(\frac{a+b}{2}\right)^2$$

(using $\text{Var}(X) = \text{E}(X^2) - \left(\text{E}(X)\right)^2$

$$= \frac{b^2 + ab + a^2}{3} - \frac{a^2 + 2ab + b^2}{4}$$

$$= \frac{4(b^2 + ab + a^2) - 3(a^2 + 2ab + b^2)}{12}$$

$$= \frac{b^2 - 2ab + a^2}{12}$$

$$= \frac{(b-a)^2}{12}$$

The CDF can be calculated as follows:

$$\begin{aligned} \text{F}(x) &= \int_a^x \text{f}(t)\,\text{d}t \\ &= \int_a^x \frac{1}{b-a}\,\text{d}t \\ &= \frac{1}{b-a}\int_a^x \text{d}t \\ &= \frac{1}{b-a}\Big[\,t\,\Big]_a^x \\ &= \frac{1}{b-a}\left(x-a\right) \\ &= \frac{x-a}{b-a} \end{aligned}$$

In full, the CDF is the following function:

$$\text{F}(x) = \begin{cases} 0 & x < a \\ \dfrac{x-a}{b-a} & a \le x \le b \\ 1 & x > b \end{cases}$$

and its graph is shown in Figure 8.2

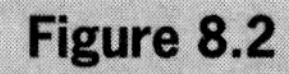
Figure 8.2

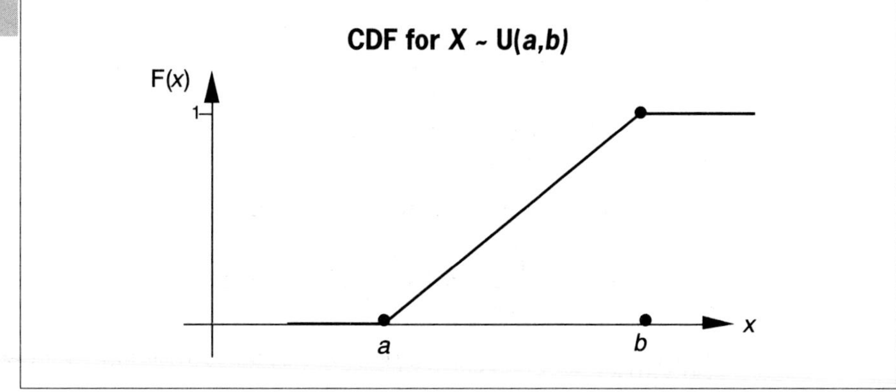

Example $X \sim U(0, 1)$. Write down $E(X)$, $Var(X)$, $f(x)$ and $F(x)$ for the random variable

Find $P(0.3 < X < 0.6)$

Solution Using the results obtained with $a = 0$ and $b = 1$ we have:

$$E(X) = \frac{0+1}{2} = \frac{1}{2}$$

$$Var(X) = \frac{(1-0)^2}{12} = \frac{1}{12}$$

$$f(x) = \begin{cases} 1 & 0 \le x \le 1 \\ 0 & \text{otherwise} \end{cases}$$

$$F(x) = \begin{cases} 0 & x < 0 \\ x & 0 \le x \le 1 \\ 1 & x > 1 \end{cases}$$

$$P(0.3 < X < 0.6) = F(0.6) - F(0.3) = 0.3$$

You should now be able to answer Exercise 1 on page 142.

The normal distribution

The **normal distribution** is the most important in statistics, for two reasons:

1 It provides a suitable model for a wide range of data.

2 It provides the theoretical basis for statistical inference.

The mathematics of the normal distribution is difficult and not required for 'A' level but we include the PDF for completeness.

A continuous random variable, X, is said to have a normal distribution when it has a PDF of the form:

$$f(x) = \frac{1}{\sigma\sqrt{2\pi}} \exp\left(-\frac{(x-\mu)^2}{2\sigma^2}\right) \quad \text{for } -\infty < x < \infty$$

where μ and σ are the parameters of the distribution and $\exp(x)$ is an alternative notation for e^x.

Since X is a random variable it follows that:

$$\int_{-\infty}^{\infty} \frac{1}{\sigma\sqrt{2\pi}} \exp\left(-\frac{(x-\mu)^2}{2\sigma^2}\right) dx = 1$$

If X is a random variable having a normal distribution, then we write $X \sim N(\mu, \sigma^2)$.

The parameters of the distribution are actually the mean and variance of the distribution, i.e.

$$E(X) = \mu \text{ and } Var(X) = \sigma^2$$

A variable which is normally distributed will typically exhibit a characteristic 'bell-shape' as illustrated in Figure 8.3.

Figure 8.3

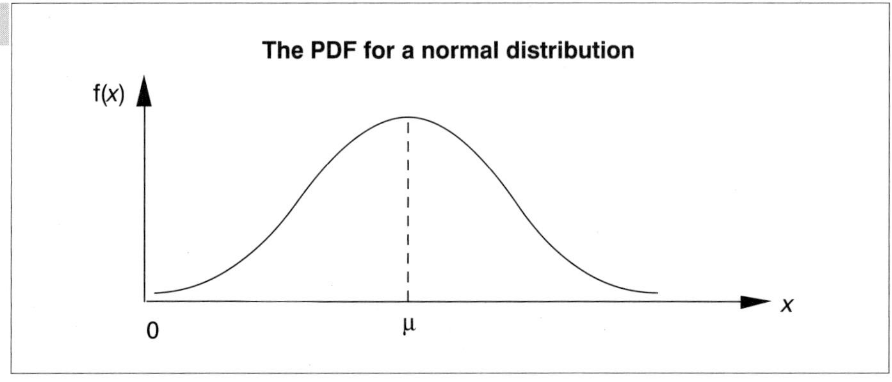

It can be seen (and shown mathematically) that the distribution is symmetrical about the mean value, μ. It is evident that the curve itself will alter depending on the two parameters μ and σ^2. It is worthwhile considering what these alterations would be.

Example

(a) Assume we have a number of normally distributed variables with the same variance but differing mean values. Draw a sketch of the distributions.

(b) Now assume these variables have the same mean but differing variances. Sketch these distributions now.

Solution

For case (a) we would expect a diagram similar to Figure 8.4 whilst for case (b) it would be similar to Figure 8.5.

Figure 8.4

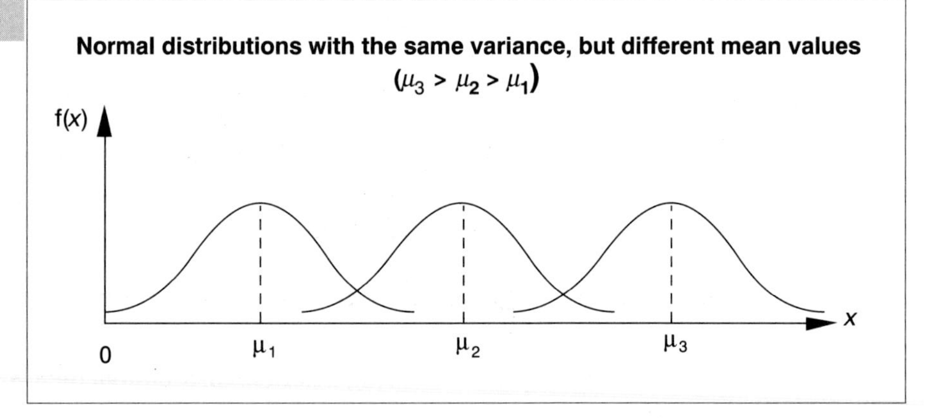

Figure 8.5

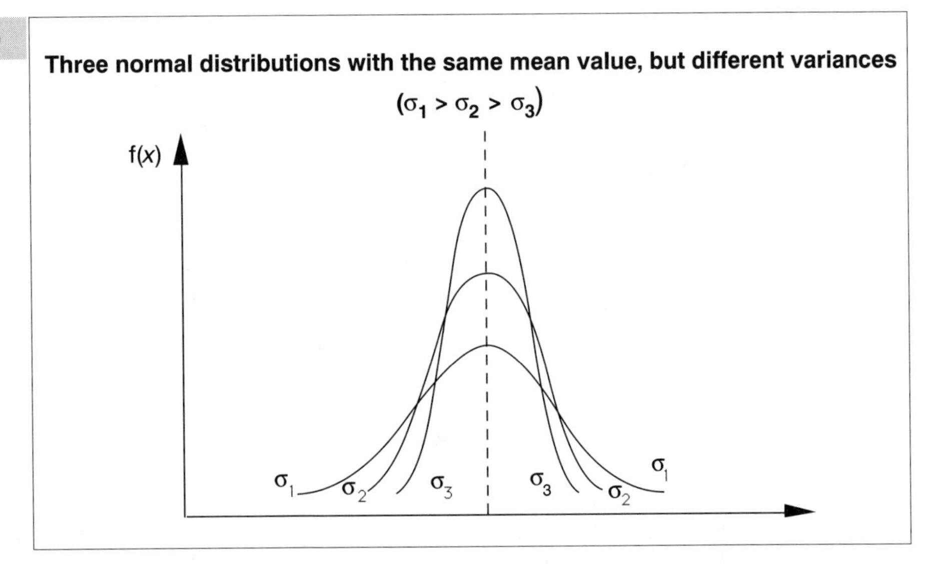

Calculation of probabilities

Let's start with an example.

Example Suppose we have a random variable $X \sim N(100, 25)$

i.e. X has a normal distribution with mean = 100 and variance = 25.

Suppose further that we need to find $P(X > 103)$.

Then we would need to find the area illustrated in Figure 8.6.

Figure 8.6

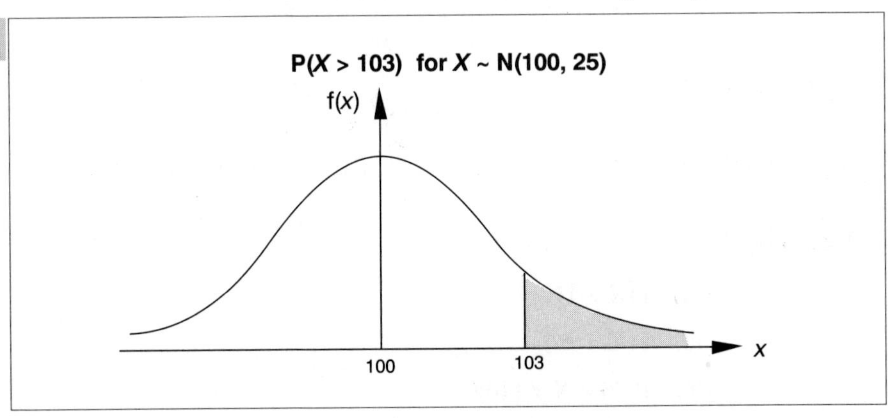

Accordingly we would need to evaluate the following integral:

$$\int_{103}^{\infty} \frac{1}{5\sqrt{2\pi}} e^{-\frac{(x-100)^2}{50}} dx$$

You will be relieved to know that the evaluation of such integrals is not necessary and that probabilities for all normal distributions are obtained from tables of the standardised normal distribution.

The standardised normal distribution

The standardised normal distribution takes advantage of the fact that all normal distributions have the same basic shape, but vary only in terms of two parameters: mean and variance. This is effectively the same as saying that all such distributions are identical except for the values of μ and σ^2.

In general if $X \sim N(\mu, \sigma^2)$

and we let $Z = \dfrac{X-\mu}{\sigma}$ then Z is N(0, 1).

Every normal distribution can be transformed into a standard normal in this way. We write $\Phi(z)$ for $P(Z \leq z)$ and it is values of $\Phi(z)$ which can be found in the table in Appendix 2 (p. 156). Φ is the Greek capital letter 'phi'.

Note:

$$\begin{aligned}
E\left(\frac{X-\mu}{\sigma}\right) &= \frac{1}{\sigma}E(X-\mu) \\
&= \frac{1}{\sigma}\left(E(X)-\mu\right) \\
&= \frac{1}{\sigma}(\mu-\mu) = 0 \\
\text{Var}\left(\frac{X-\mu}{\sigma}\right) &= \text{Var}\left(\frac{X}{\sigma}\right) + \text{Var}\left(\frac{\mu}{\sigma}\right) \\
&= \frac{1}{\sigma^2}\,\text{Var}(X) \\
&= \frac{1}{\sigma^2} \times \sigma^2 = 1
\end{aligned}$$

We will now see how to calculate normal probabilities by an example.

Example If $X \sim N(100, 25)$, find:

(a) $P(X > 110)$

(b) $P(X < 95)$

(c) $P(95 < X < 110)$

Solution

The first step *always* when finding normal probabilities is to standardise the random variable.

Let $Z = \dfrac{X - 100}{5}$

(Note that the denominator of this fraction is σ whereas the parameter of the distribution is σ^2.)

(a) $P(X > 110) = P\left(Z > \dfrac{110 - 100}{5}\right) = P(Z > 2)$

We have transformed the problem from

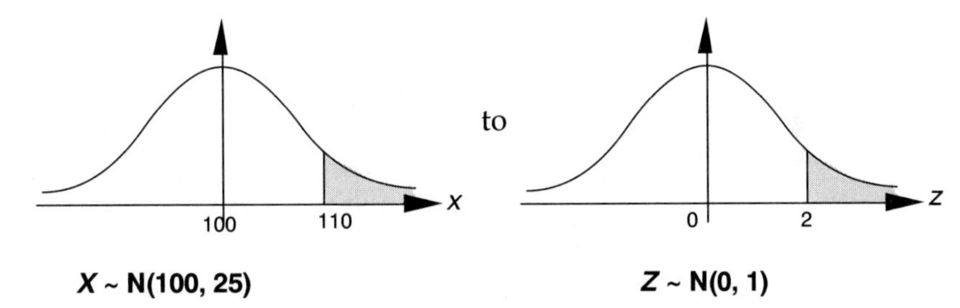

The diagram illustrates the fact that $P(X > 110) = P(Z > 2)$

Now we need the tables in Appendix 2.

The left-hand column gives values for Z. It is important to notice that the table gives probabilities of the form $P(Z < z)$ where z is a positive value. In order to calculate probabilities not of this form we use the symmetry of the curve and the fact that the total area under the curve is 1 as appropriate.

For $P(Z > 2)$ we use the fact that the total area under the curve is 1 and find $1 - P(Z \leq 2)$, or equivalently $P(Z < 2)$, since $P(Z = 2) = 0$ for a continuous distribution:

i.e. $P(Z > 2) = 1 - P(Z \leq 2)$

$\Rightarrow P(Z > 2) = 1 - \Phi(2) = 1 - 0.9772$

$\Rightarrow P(Z > 2) = 0.0228$

$\Rightarrow P(X > 110) = 0.023$ (3 d.p.)

(b) $P(X < 95)$

$= P\left(Z < \dfrac{95 - 100}{5}\right)$

$= P(Z < -1)$

Now for $P(Z < -1)$ we cannot use the tables directly, but by symmetry

$$P(Z < -1) = P(Z > 1)$$

The problem has been transformed from:

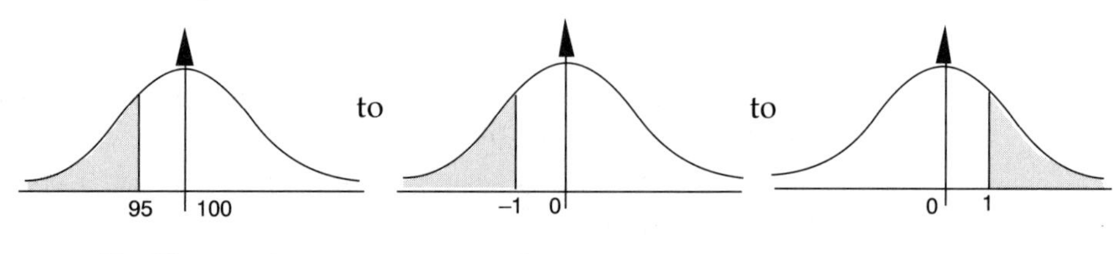

$X \sim N(100, 25)$ $Z \sim N(0, 1)$ $Z \sim N(0, 1)$

So $P(Z < -1) = 1 - P(Z \leq 1)$

(using the fact that the total area is 1)

$$= 1 - \Phi(1) = 1 - 0.8413 = 0.1587$$

Hence $P(X < 95) = 0.159$ (3 d.p.)

(c) $P(95 < X < 110) = P\left(\frac{95 - 100}{5} < Z < \frac{110 - 100}{5}\right)$

$$= P(-1 < Z < 2)$$

So now we have to find:

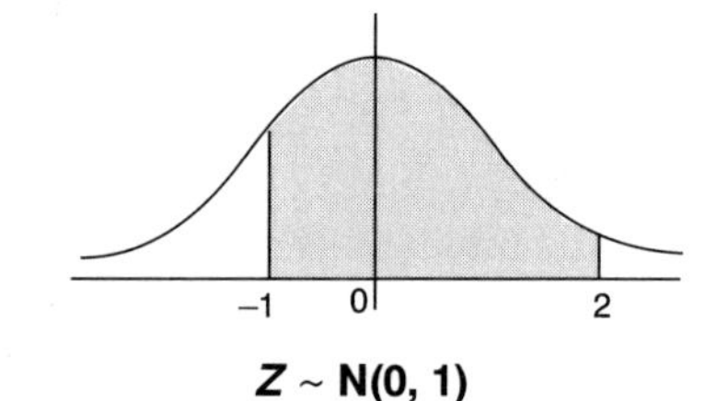

$Z \sim N(0, 1)$

Clearly from our answers to (a) and (b) this will be

$$1 - 0.023 - 0.159 = 0.818$$

i.e. $P(95 < X < 110) = 0.82$ (2 d.p.)

It is important to be able to use normal distribution tables efficiently and correctly. It should also be noted that not all normal distribution tables have the same format as the ones we are using (although they are the ones used by ULEAC).

If in doubt look at the diagram below the body of the tables to see which probabilities are being given. It is also worth noting that a simple sketch of the areas being found is a useful device and can help decide whether answers obtained are sensible.

Example

In an examination it is known that the distribution of marks is N(52, 24).

(a) What proportion of marks will exceed 55?

(b) What proportion of marks will be less than 45?

(c) If Grade A is to be awarded to the top 5% of marks, what mark must someone achieve to get this grade?

(d) The bottom 20% of marks are classed as Grade F. What range of marks does this represent?

Solution

(a) For marks greater than 55:

$$X > 55 \Rightarrow Z > \frac{55 - 52}{4.9} = 0.61$$

giving a probability value of $P(Z < 0.61) = 0.7291$. But we require $P(Z > 0.61)$ hence we have a probability of $(1 - 0.7291) = 0.2709$. That is, just over 27% of marks will exceed 55.

(b) For marks less than 45 we have $Z \leq -1.43$

By symmetry, $P(Z \leq -1.43) = P(Z \geq 1.43)$ (see diagrams below)

$$= 1 - \Phi(1.43) = 1 - 0.9236$$
$$= 0.0764 \text{ or almost } 8\%.$$

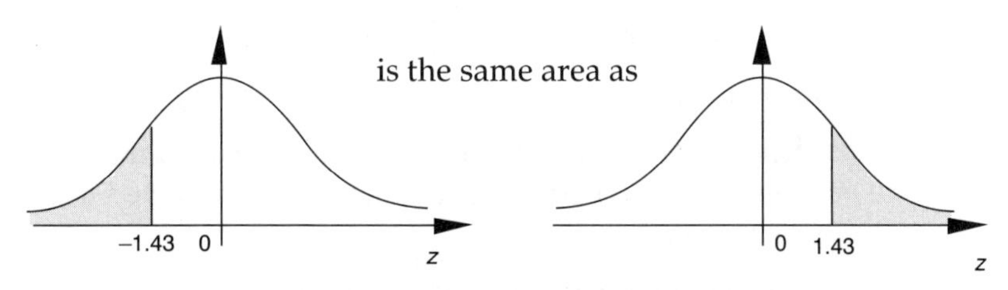

(c) To find the top 5% mark requires a different approach. This time we know the proportion (5% or 0.05, corresponding to a probability of 0.95) but require the x-value that corresponds to this. Searching through the table we see that the z value corresponding to 0.95 is 1.645 (given that z values of 1.64 and 1.65 are both equidistant). So we have:

$$z = 1.645 = \frac{x - 52}{4.9} \quad \text{which gives } x = 60.06$$

In other words a mark of 60 or more will be achieved by 5% of people taking the exam.

(d) A similar approach can now be adopted to find the bottom 20% mark. For 20% (or 0.20) the nearest corresponding z value is 0.84. But remembering which side of the distribution we are looking at this implies:

$$z = -0.84 = \frac{x - 52}{4.9} \quad \text{which gives } x = 47.88$$

If we rounded this to give a practical result we would say a mark below 48 would be graded as F.

You should now attempt Exercises 2–4 on pages 142–43.

Using the normal distribution to approximate the binomial and Poisson

Just as we can, under certain conditions, use the Poisson to approximate the binomial distribution, so we can use the normal distribution to approximate to the binomial and Poisson distributions.

Normal approximation to the binomial distribution

Recall that if X is binomial with parameters n and p $\left(\text{i.e. } X \sim \text{B}(n, p)\right)$ then $\text{E}(X) = np$, $\text{Var}(X) = np\,(1 - p)$

Now if n is fairly large (> 10) and p is fairly close to 0.5, the binomial distribution can be approximated by a normal distribution having the same mean and variance.

i.e. $\quad X \sim \text{B}(n, p) \Rightarrow X \approx \text{N}\left(np, np\,(1 - p)\right)$

where $\approx$ means 'is approximately distributed'.

Now, the binomial distribution is discrete and the normal distribution is continuous so better approximations are obtained using a continuity correction.

We now illustrate this with an example.

Example X is the number of heads obtained when a coin is tossed 20 times. Find:

(a) $\text{P}(X \leq 13)$

(b) $\text{P}(X < 13)$

(c) $\text{P}(X > 13)$

(d) $\text{P}(X \geq 13)$

(e) $\text{P}(X = 13)$

For part (e) we will also check the accuracy of the result.

Solution

We could obtain each of these probabilities using the exact distribution, i.e. $X \sim B(20, \frac{1}{2})$. However, this would be a laborious calculation:

$$P(X \le 13) = P(X = 0) + P(X = 1) + (P(X = 2) + \dots + P(X = 13)$$

Fortunately, we can get very close to the correct answer by using the normal approximation.

Firstly note that:

$$X \sim B(20, \tfrac{1}{2}) \Rightarrow X \approx N\left(20 \times \tfrac{1}{2}, 20 \times \tfrac{1}{2} \times \tfrac{1}{2}\right)$$

i.e. $X \approx N(10, 5)$

and that the parameters of the binomial are suitable for such an approximation to be made.

(a) $P(X \le 13)$

Consider Figure 8.7.

Figure 8.7

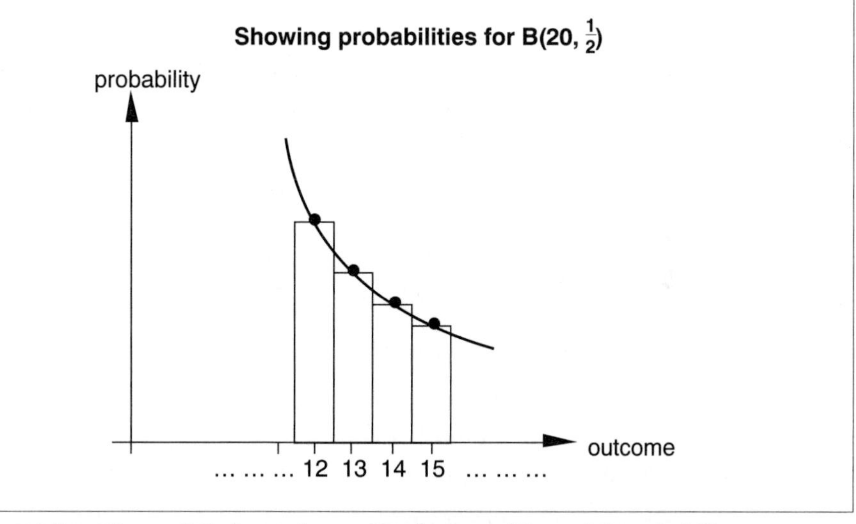

Now Figure 8.7 shows how calculating a binomial probability amounts to adding up chunks of discrete probability. The curve which approximates these, as shown in the diagram, would pass through the mid-points of the tops of the bars and finding $P(X \le 13)$ from the curve would miss half of the bar for $X = 13$.

For this reason we apply a continuity correction and find $P(X \le 13.5)$ as it will give a better approximation than would finding $P(X \le 13)$.

The problem now is:

for the distribution $X \approx N(10, 5)$

find $P(X \le 13.5)$

Let $Z = \dfrac{X-10}{\sqrt{5}}$ then $Z \sim N(0, 1)$

$$P(X \le 13.5) = P\left(Z \le \frac{13.5-10}{\sqrt{5}}\right)$$

$= P(Z \le 1.57)$

$= 0.9418$ from the tables

Hence P(13 or less heads) ≈ 0.94 (2 d.p.)

(The correct answer to 4 d.p. is 0.9423 and so the approximation is exact to 2 d.p.)

(b) $P(X < 13)$

Now the first step is to write $P(X \le 12)$ which, in a discrete distribution, is the same and then we can use the approximating distribution N(10, 5) and find $P(X \le 12.5)$.

Using results from (a)

$$P(X \le 12.5) = P\left(Z \le \frac{12.5-10}{\sqrt{5}}\right) = P(Z \le 1.12)$$

$= 0.8686$ (from the tables)

So P(less than 13 trials) $= 0.87$ (2 d.p.)

(c) $P(X > 13)$

$= 1 - P(X \le 13)$

$\approx 1 - P(X \le 13.5)$ (using continuity correction)

$= 1 - 0.94$ (using (a))

$= 0.06$

i.e. P(more than 13 heads) ≈ 0.06

(d) $P(X \ge 13)$

$= 1 - P(X \le 12)$

$\approx 1 - P(X \le 12.5)$ (using continuity correction)

$= 1 - 0.87$ (using (b))

$= 0.13$

i.e. P(13 or more heads) ≈ 0.13

(e) For $P(X = 13)$ using a normal approximation directly would give a zero answer since for any continuous distribution the probability of an individual outcome is always zero.

To get round this problem we could approximate $P(X = 13)$ by $P(12.5 \leq X \leq 13.5)$

i.e. use a continuity correction in both directions (in fact for more accuracy we could use $P(12.1 \leq X \leq 13.1)$).

But: $P(12.5 \leq X \leq 13.5)$ for $X \approx N(10, 5)$ gives

$$P\left(\frac{12.5 - 10}{\sqrt{5}} \leq Z \leq \frac{13.5 - 10}{\sqrt{5}}\right)$$

$$= P(1.12 \leq Z \leq 1.57)$$

$$= 0.9418 - 0.8686 = 0.07 \text{ (2 d.p.)}$$

The exact answer is $\binom{20}{13}\left(\frac{1}{2}\right)^{13}\left(\frac{1}{2}\right)^{7} = 0.0739$ (4 d.p.)

so the approximation is good.

In conclusion if we have $X \sim B(n, p)$ and we wish to find $P(X \leq x)$ by using a normal approximation, then we use the distribution

$$X \approx N(np, np(1 - p))$$

and find $P\left(X \leq x + \frac{1}{2}\right)$ using a continuity correction. The approximation is appropriate for $n > 10$ and $p \approx \frac{1}{2}$

Note: We saw in the last example that *all* discrete probabilities can be re-formulated to be given in terms of probabilities of the required form and this should always be the first step.

You should now practise your understanding of this section by working through Exercises 5–6 on page 143.

Normal approximation to Poisson

If $X \sim P(\mu)$ and μ is large (say, $\mu > 10$) then we can find approximate values for the Poisson probabilities by using a normal distribution with the same mean and variance and using a continuity correction as in the last case since we are again approximating a discrete distribution by a continuous one.

The result is:

if $X \sim P(\mu)$ then $X \approx N(\mu, \mu)$

provided μ is sufficiently large ($\mu > 10$ will give reasonable approximations)

Example If $X \sim P(15)$ find $P(X > 21)$

(a) using the Poisson formula

(b) using the normal approximation

Solution (a) $P(X > 21) = P(X = 22) + P(X = 23) + \ldots\ldots$

which is very tedious to work out (and working out the complement would be almost as tedious). But we will work out a few terms of this:

$$P(X = 22) = \frac{e^{-15} \times 15^{22}}{22!} = 0.0204$$

$$P(X = 23) = \frac{e^{-15} \times 15^{23}}{23!} = 0.0133$$

$$P(X = 24) = \frac{e^{-15} \times 15^{24}}{24!} = 0.0083$$

$$P(X = 25) = \frac{e^{-15} \times 15^{25}}{25!} = 0.0050$$

$$P(X = 26) = \frac{e^{-15} \times 15^{26}}{26!} = 0.0029$$

and successive probabilities tend rapidly to zero

so $P(X > 21) \approx 0.05$ (2 d.p.)

(b) To apply the normal approximation, we will write $P(X > 21)$ as $P(X \geq 21.5)$ which is $1 - P(X \leq 21)$. We apply the continuity correction to this so that we work out:

$$1 - P(X \leq 21.5)$$

from the distribution N(15, 15)

Let $Z = \dfrac{X - 15}{\sqrt{15}}$

Then $P(X \leq 21.5) = P\left(Z \leq \dfrac{21.5 - 15}{\sqrt{15}}\right)$

$= P(Z \leq 1.68) = 0.9535$ (from tables)

So $1 - P(X \leq 21.5) = 0.0465 \approx 0.05$ (2 d.p.)

So the approximating distribution was accurate to 2 d.p in this example.

In conclusion, if $X \sim P(\mu)$ and $\mu > 10$, to find $P(X \leq r)$, the approximating distribution $X \approx N(\mu,\mu)$ can be used and increased accuracy will be obtained by using the continuity correction and finding $P(X \leq r + \frac{1}{2})$.

Linear combinations of independent normal random variables

A remarkable and useful property of normal random variables which are independent is that we can form combinations of them which are themselves normal. These combinations are formed by the following rules which need to be remembered.

If $X_1 \sim N(\mu_1, \sigma_1^2)$ and $X_2 \sim N(\mu_2, \sigma_2^2)$

are independent normal random variables,

then $X_1 + X_2 \sim N(\mu_1 + \mu_2, \sigma_1^2 + \sigma_2^2)$

and $X_1 - X_2 \sim N(\mu_1 - \mu_2, \sigma_1^2 + \sigma_2^2)$

where it should be noted that the new means and variances follow the rules stated in Section 6.

More generally these rules extend to any linear combinations of normal random variables as follows:

If $X_1 \sim N(\mu_1, \sigma_1^2), X_2 \sim N(\mu_2, \sigma_2^2) \ldots X_n \sim N(\mu_n, \sigma_n^2)$

and $a_1, a_2, \ldots a_n$ are any real numbers,

then we can form a new random variable:

$$a_1X_1 + a_2X_2 + \ldots + a_nX_n \sim N(a_1\mu_1 + a_2\mu_2 + \ldots + a_n\mu_n, a_1^2\sigma_1^2 + a_2^2\sigma_2^2 + \ldots + a_n^2\sigma_n^2)$$

The usefulness of this result is apparent in the following problem.

Example Adult male heights are distributed N(168,12) and adult female heights are distributed N(164,10).

Find the probability that a randomly chosen female is taller than a randomly chosen male.

Solution Let $M \sim N(168,12)$
and $F \sim N(164,10)$

then we require $P(F > M) = P(F - M > 0)$.

Now $F - M$ is a new normal random variable and provided that male and female heights are independent (there is no reason to suppose otherwise), we can use the results above to state that $F - M$ has a normal distribution with parameters that we can easily calculate.

Let $\quad D = F - M$

then $\quad D \sim N(164 - 168, 10 + 12)$

i.e. $\quad D \sim N(-4, 22)$

and we require $P(D > 0)$

Let $\quad Z = \dfrac{D - (-4)}{\sqrt{22}} = \dfrac{D + 4}{\sqrt{22}}$

then as usual,

$$Z \sim N(0, 1)$$

$$\begin{aligned} P(D > 0) &= P(\sqrt{22}\,Z - 4 > 0) \\ &= P\left(Z > \frac{4}{\sqrt{22}}\right) = P(Z > 0.853) \\ &= 1 - \Phi(0.853) \quad = 1 - 0.8023 \quad = 0.198 \end{aligned}$$

You should now be able to attempt Exercises 7–10 on pages 143–45.

EXERCISES

1 $X \sim U(-1, 3)$ i.e. X has a continuous uniform distribution defined on the interval $-1 \le x \le 3$. For this distribution find $E(X)$, $Var(X)$, $P(X > 0)$, $F(x)$, the CDF, and sketch the PDF and CDF.

2 Find the shaded areas in the following normal distributions:

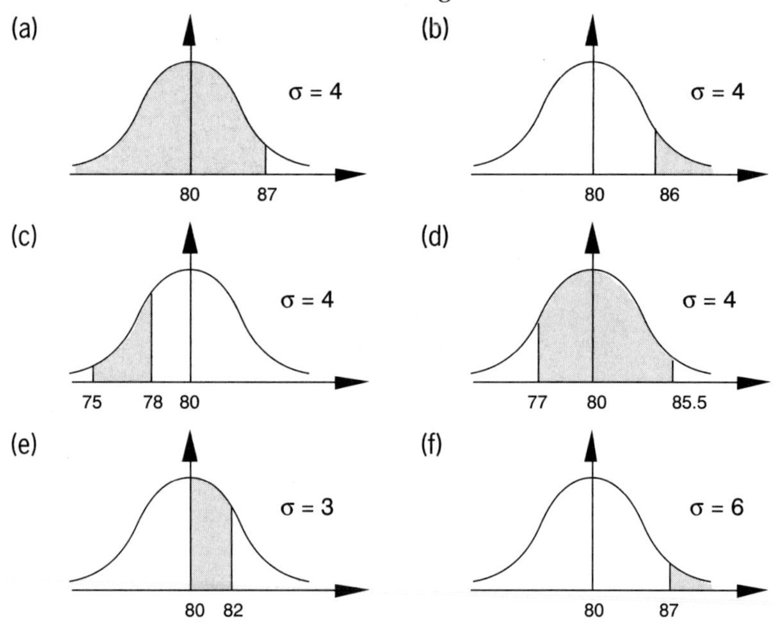

3 Find the value of x in each of the following normal distributions:

(a)

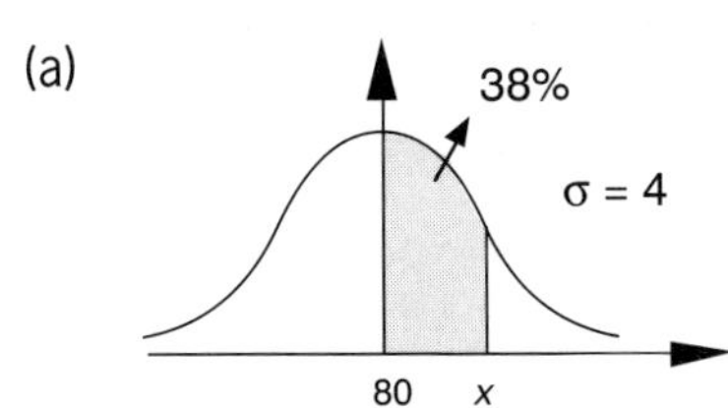

(b)

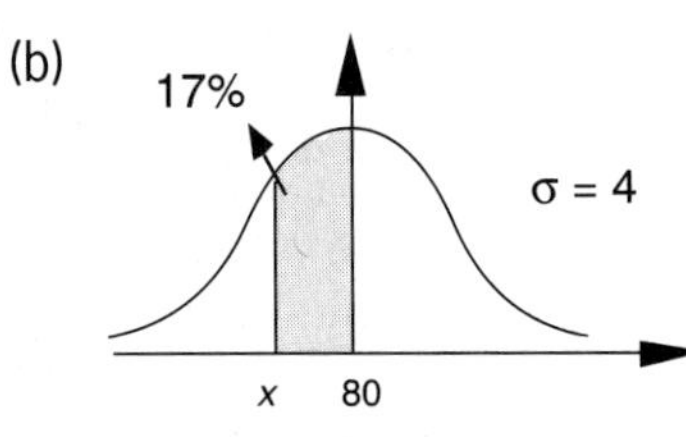

(c)

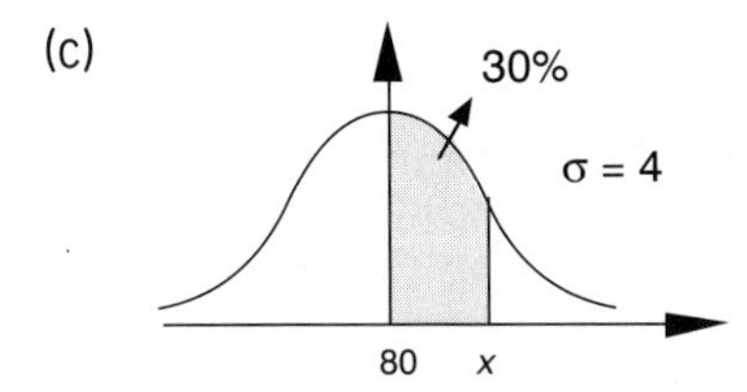

(d)

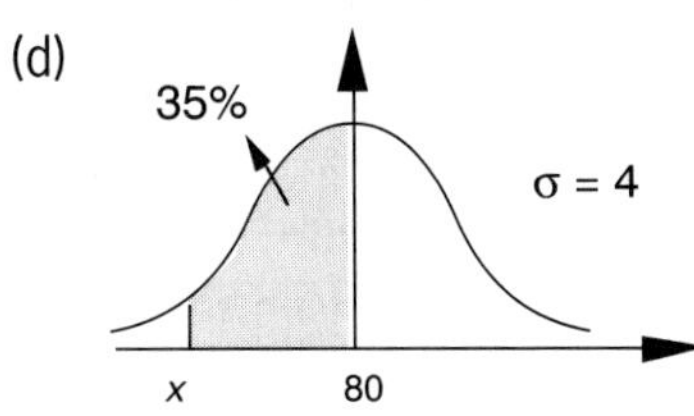

4 (a) $X \sim N(\mu, 25)$ and $P(X < 32) = 0.6$. Find μ.

(b) $X \sim N(40, \sigma^2)$ and $P(X > 37) = 0.7$. Find σ.

(c) $X \sim N(\mu, \sigma^2)$ and it is known that:

$P(X < 22) = 0.74$

$P(X > 17) = 0.78$

Find μ and σ^2.

5 $X \sim B(200, 0.45)$

Find approximations (using continuity correction) to the following:

(a) $P(X \leq 76)$

(b) $P(X > 110)$

(c) $P(80 \leq X < 100)$

6 40% of males need glasses.

(a) Choose a sample of 7 males.
Find P(more than 3 need glasses).

(b) Choose a sample of 700 males.
Find P(more than 300 need glasses).

7 With a computer you expect an average of 3 errors for every ten thousand characters transmitted.

(a) 5000 characters are transmitted.
Find P(no errors).

(b) 1 million characters are transmitted.
Find P(no more than 280 errors).

8 A statistics student studied young children's ability to estimate. Each child was presented with a straight line AB of length 12 cm drawn on a piece of paper. The child was required to put a mark X on the line where he or she believed the mid-point of AB was.

As a preliminary model of this experiment the student assumed that the child would mark the point X in such a way that the distance AX had a uniform distribution over the interval [3, 9].

(a) Calculate the mean and variance of the distance AX using this model.

The student tested 100 children and the results obtained can be summarised as follows: $\Sigma x = 590$ and $\Sigma x^2 = 3571$, where x is the distance AX in centimetres.

(b) Calculate the mean and variance of AX for the student's data.

(c) Explain briefly why the student may wish to alter the model in the light of these findings.

The student studied the results for the 100 children again and noticed that 5 children had AX smaller than 4.3 cm and 17 had AX more than 6.9 cm.

(d) Assuming that AX has a normal distribution with mean μ and variance σ^2, use this new information above to estimate the values of μ and σ^2.

(e) Compare your estimates in (d) with the values found in (b) and comment on the suitability of the normal distribution as a model for this experiment.

9 Jam is packed in tins of nominal net weight 1 kg. The actual weight of jam delivered to a tin by the filling machine is normally distributed about the mean weight set on the machine with a standard deviation of 12 g.

The average filling of jam is 1 kg.

(a) Find the probability that a tin chosen at random contains less than 985 g.

It is a legal requirement that no more than 1% of tins contain less than the nominal weight.

(b) Find the minimum setting of the filling machine which will meet this requirement.

10 Audrey is a regular customer of Toto's taxis. When she rings from home the time, X, a taxi takes to arrive is normally distributed with mean 19 minutes, standard deviation 3 minutes.

(a) (i) What is the probability of her having to wait less than 15 minutes for a taxi?

(ii) What waiting time will be exceeded with a probability of 0.1?

Audrey decides to try Blue Star taxis. The standard deviation of her waiting time, Y, is 7 minutes and the probability of Y exceeding 8 minutes is 0.97725.

(b) Find the mean of Y, assuming a normal distribution.

(c) What is the distribution of T where $T = Y - X$? (X and Y may be assumed independent.)

If both firms were rung at the same time what is the probability that Toto would arrive first?

(d) In order to catch a train Audrey needs a taxi within 10 minutes. Which firm would you advise her to ring? Explain your answer.

[AEB 1993]

SUMMARY

Now you have completed this section you should understand:

- the continuous uniform distribution
- the normal distribution and the calculation of normal probabilities using the standardised distribution Z
- how, in certain conditions, the normal can be used to approximate to the binomial and Poisson distributions (in both cases a continuity correction has to be made).

MODULE

T1

Solutions

Section 1

1 There are a number of reasons that spring to mind. Such a data collection exercise would:

- take too much time
- be very difficult to organise
- be very costly
- provide too much data for us to analyse
- probably be out of date by the time it was completed.

2 (a) (i) The population may be very large and/or inaccessible.

Costs are kept lower.

Results are more quickly obtained.

The testing might destroy the sample.

(ii) A sampling frame is a list of all the members of a population.

(b) A list of all the pupils in the school.

3 (a) continuous

(b) qualitative

(c) discrete

(d) discrete

(e) continuous

(f) continuous

Section 2

1 A frequency table for females would look like this:

Heights (cm)	Number of females
150–	2
155–	7
160–	10
165–	13
170–	15
175–	2
180–	1
185–	0
Total frequency	50

2 Below is a frequency table for females showing relative and cumulative frequencies:

Heights (cm)	No. of females	Relative frequency	Cumulative frequency
150–	2	0.04	2
155–	7	0.14	9
160–	10	0.20	19
165–	13	0.26	32
170–	15	0.30	47
175–	2	0.04	49
180–	1	0.02	50
185–	0	0.00	50
Total	50	1.00	50

3 You should have a diagram similar to this:

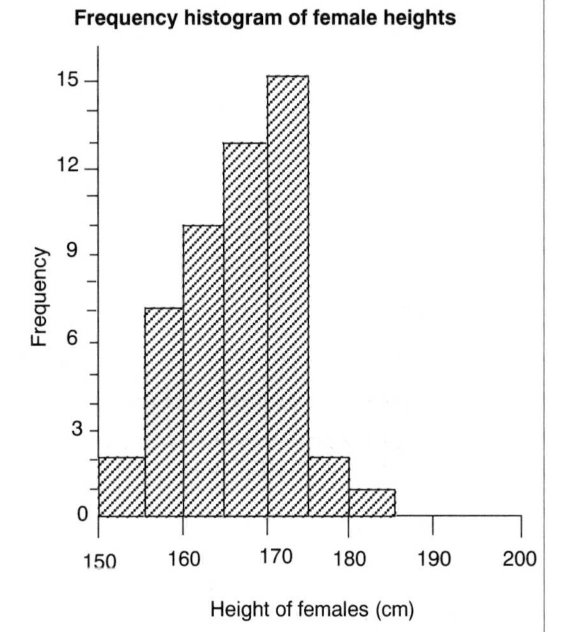

4 The stem and leaf diagrams look like this:

(a)

0	2 6
1	2 2 5 8
2	0 0 7
3	1 8
4	2

(b)

0.	5 9
1.	0 2 5 6 8
2.	1 2 3 5 8 9
3.	0 2 3 4 7
4.	2 8

5 For females:

lowest value ≈ 150 cm
highest value ≈ 185 cm
lower quartile ≈ 162 cm
upper quartile ≈ 172 cm
median ≈ 168 cm

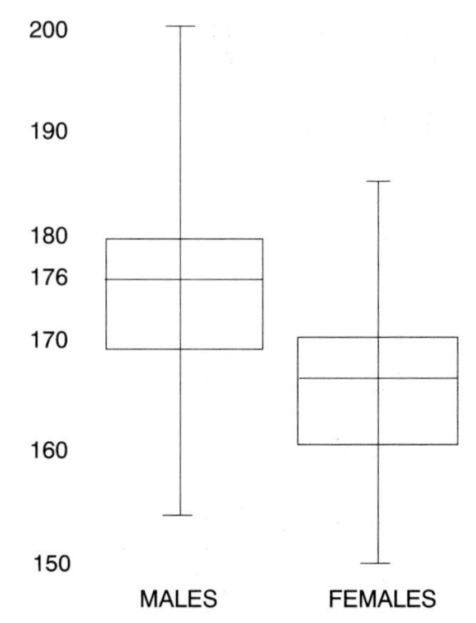

This clearly shows that females are on average shorter than males. The middle 50% of females are approximately 10 cm shorter than the middle 50% of males.

6 Since the data is continuous, it is really as in the following table.

		Length of interval	As a multiple of 5	Adjusted frequency
9.5–19.5	20	10	5×2	10
19.5–24.5	20	5	5×1	20
24.5–29.5	15	5	5×1	15
29.5–30.5	14	1	5×0.2	70
30.5–34.5	16	4	5×0.8	20
34.5–39.5	10	5	5×1	10
39.5–59.5	10	20	5×4	2.5

The above method takes 5 as a unit on the horizontal axis and adjusts frequencies accordingly.

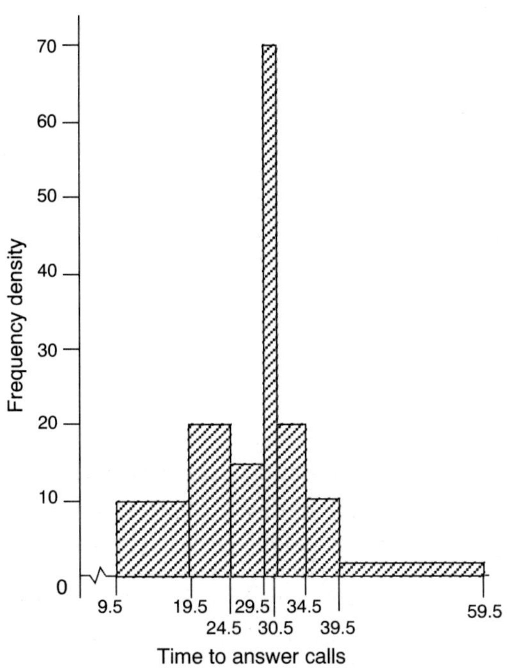

The reason for using a histogram is that the data is continuous.

7 No vertical scale given.

No adjustment in heights of bars for differing widths of intervals.

$$\text{Median} = 5 + \frac{13}{65} \times 5 \approx 6.0$$

The number experiencing delays of less than 4.7 minutes

$$= 35 + 34 + 50 + \left(\frac{1.7}{2} \times 36\right)$$

$$= 149.6 \approx 50\%$$

8 The frequency table is shown below:

Class	Class width	Frequency	Frequency density
0–4	5	4462	892.4
5–15	11	12,214	1110.4
16–24	9	10,898	1210.9
25–44	20	19,309	965.5
45–74	30	22,820	760.7
75–95	21	3364	160.2

This gives the following histogram.

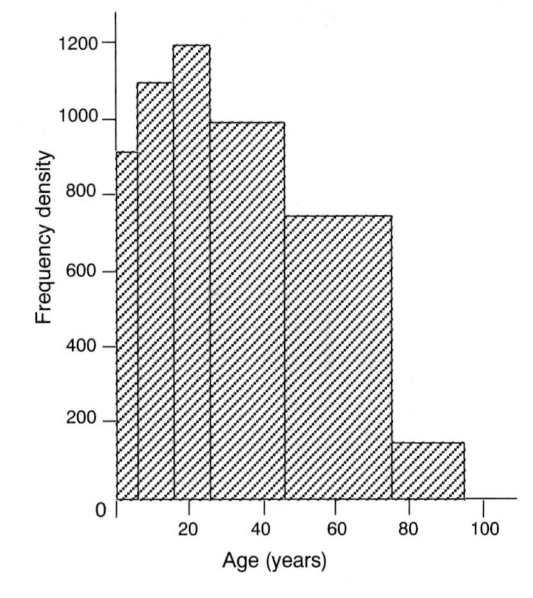

Section 3

1 The appropriate calculations for females summarise to:

$$\text{Mean} = \frac{\Sigma fx}{\Sigma f} = \frac{8335.0}{50} = 166.7 \text{ cm}$$

The reason why the mean based on aggregated data is different from that based on raw data is explained on page 30.

2 $\text{Mean} = \frac{\Sigma x}{n} = \frac{54}{9} = 6$

$\text{Median} = \frac{9+1}{2} = 5\text{th value}$

In increasing order the set becomes

2 3 4 6 $\underline{\underline{7}}$ 7 8 8 9

$\therefore$ Median = 7

3 $\text{Mean} = \frac{\Sigma x}{n} = \frac{42}{6} = 7$

$\text{Median} = \frac{6+1}{2} = 3.5\text{th value}$

In increasing order the set becomes

1 4 6 8 11 12

$\therefore \text{Median} = \frac{6+8}{2} = 7$

4 $\bar{x} =$

\f(5 × 2 + 6 × 7 + 7 × 12 + 8 × 10 + 9 × 5 + 10 × 4,2 + 7 + 12 + 10 + 5 + 4)

$= \frac{301}{40} = 7.53 \text{ (2 d.p.)}$

5 Mean =

$$\frac{2 \times 3 + 6 \times 8 + 10 \times 19 + 14 \times 14 + 18 \times 6}{50}$$

$= \frac{548}{50} = 10.96$

$\text{Median} = 8 + (25.5 - 11)\frac{4}{19} = 11.1$

6 (a) Put $y = x - 235$

Then we have

y	0–5	6–15	16–25	26–30
Freq	12	40	45	8

$$\bar{y} = \frac{3 \times 12 + 11 \times 40 + 21 \times 45 + 28.5 \times 8}{12 + 40 + 45 + 8}$$

$= \frac{1649}{105} = 15.7$

Now since $\bar{y} = \bar{x} - 235$, we have

$\bar{x} = \bar{y} + 235 = 250.7$

(b) Put $y = \frac{x - 35\,000}{10}$

Then y consists of

{ 735, 189, 2635, 1840, 1361 }

So $\bar{y} = \frac{6760}{5} = 1352$

Now since $\bar{y} = \frac{\bar{x} - 35\,000}{10}$, we have

$\bar{x} = 10\bar{y} + 35\,000$

$= 13\,520 + 35\,000 = 48\,520$

7 (a) $\bar{x} + a$

(b) $b\bar{x}$

8 $\bar{x}_A =$

$$\frac{39 \times 5 + 25 \times 2 + 80 \times 2 + 140 \times 3 + 125 \times 1}{5 + 2 + 2 + 3 + 1}$$

$= \frac{950}{13} = 73.08\text{p}$

$\bar{x}_B =$

$$\frac{45 \times 5 + 23 \times 2 + 65 \times 2 + 130 \times 3 + 175 \times 1}{5 + 2 + 2 + 3 + 1}$$

$= \frac{966}{13} = 74.31\text{p}$

So, as measured by this statistic, shop A is slightly cheaper.

Section 4

1 (a) (i) $\bar{x} = \frac{55}{5} = 11$

So the deviations are –9, –4, 1, 2, 10

$\Rightarrow s^2 = \frac{1}{n}\Sigma(x - \bar{x})^2$

$= \frac{1}{5}(81 + 16 + 1 + 4 + 100) = \frac{202}{5} = 40.4$

$\Rightarrow s = 6.36$ (2 d.p.)

(ii) $\Sigma x^2 = 4 + 49 + 144 + 169 + 441 = 807$

$\Rightarrow s^2 = \frac{807}{5} - 11^2 = 40.4$

$\Rightarrow s = 6.36$ (2 d.p.)

(b) We shall use a table which will supply the columns needed for both methods.

x	f	fx	$x-\bar{x}$	$(x-\bar{x})^2$	$f(x-\bar{x})^2$	fx^2 $(= xfx)$
4	3	12	–2	4	12	48
5	8	40	–1	1	8	200
6	12	72	0	0	0	432
7	10	70	1	1	10	490
8	2	16	2	4	8	128
	35	210			38	1298

(i) $\bar{x} = \frac{210}{35} = 6$

$s^2 = \frac{38}{35} = 1.09 \Rightarrow s = 1.04$ (2 d.p.)

(ii) $s^2 = \frac{1298}{35} - 6^2 = 1.09$

$\Rightarrow s = 1.04$ (2 d.p.)

2 $s = 6.58$ cm

3

x	f	mid-interval x	fx	fx^2 $(= xfx)$
5–	4	7.5	30	225
10–	9	12.5	112.5	1406.25
15–	15	17.5	262.5	4593.75
20–	13	22.5	292.5	6581.25
25–	7	27.5	192.5	5293.75
30–	3	32.5	97.5	3168.75
	51		987.5	21268.75

$\bar{x} = \frac{987.5}{51} = 19.36$ (2 d.p.)

$s^2 = \frac{21268.75}{51} - 19.36^2 = 42.12$

4 (a) $\bar{x}_A = \frac{550}{10} = 55$ kg

$s^2{}_A = \frac{32\,500}{10} - 55^2 = 225$ kg^2

$\bar{x}_B = \frac{970}{15} = 64.67$kg

$s^2{}_B = \frac{63\,500}{15} - 64.67^2 = 51.56$ kg^2

(b) $\bar{x} = \frac{550 + 970}{10 + 15} = 60.8$ kg

$s^2 = \frac{32\,500 + 63\,500}{10 + 15} - 60.8^2 = 143.36$ kg^2

5 Advantage: easier to discern shape, centre and spread

Disadvantage: loss of accuracy and detail.

Median	27–28 cm
Upper quartile	31–32 cm
Lower quartile	23–24 cm
IQR	7 to 9 cm

Calculation gives:
Median = 27.6 cm
IQR = 8.8 cm
Median for spruce > Median for larch
IQR's are similar
Range is greater for larch than spruce

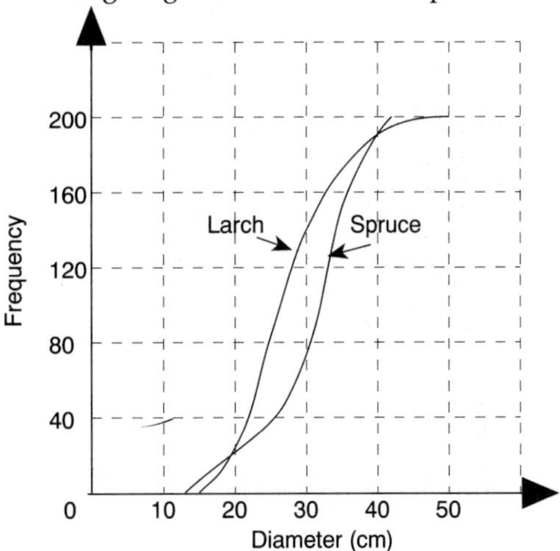

6 (a) $178 - 149 = 29$

(b) (i) lower quartile = 8.54 to 8.56

(ii) 81st percentile = 11.35 to 11.55

7 (a)

0	2 3 3 3 4 4 4 5 5 5 5 5 5 6 6 7 8 8 8 9
1	0 0 0 2 3 3 3 4 4 4 4 5 7 7 9
2	1 2 2 3 3 3 3 4 6
3	3 4 4 6
4	1 3

(b) Positively skewed

(c) $\bar{x} = \dfrac{738}{50} = 14.76$

$s^2 = \dfrac{16\,526}{50} - 14.76^2 = 112.66$

(d) Accuracy is reduced by grouping since detail is lost once all data in an interval is assumed to be concentrated at the centre of the interval.

8 (a) Skewness will be positive if the median is nearer to lower quartile than upper quartile and negative for vice versa. Equidistant $\Rightarrow$ symmetrical distribution.

(b) $\sum f = 180$

Mass < 39 $\sum f = 37$

Mass < 44 $\sum f - 71$

Hence lower quartile in interval 40–44

Linear interpolation gives:

$39.5 + \dfrac{8}{34} \times 5 \approx 40.7$

Mass < 44 $\sum f = 71$

Mass < 49 $\sum f = 110$

$\Rightarrow$ Median in interval 45–49

Linear interpolation gives:

$44.5 + \dfrac{19}{39} \times 5 = 46.9$

Mass < 49 $\sum f = 110$

Mass < 59 $\sum f = 152$

$\Rightarrow$ upper quartile in interval 50–59

Linear interpolation gives:

$49.5 + \dfrac{25}{42} \times 10 = 55.5$

Upper quartile – median = 8.5

Median – lower quartile = 6.3

$\Rightarrow$ positively skewed.

(c) The box and whisker plot looks like this:

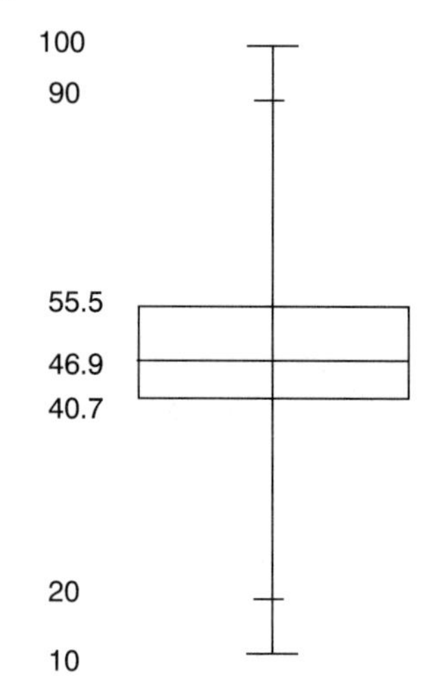

9 (a)

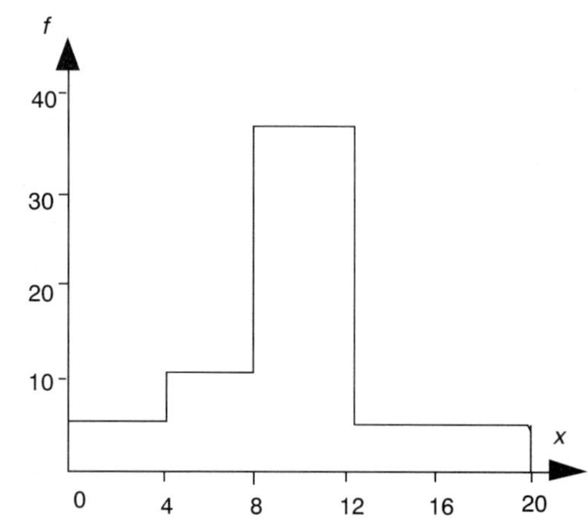

(Note that 4 is plotted for the range 12–20.) The modal class is 8–12.

(b)

Ends	4	8	12	20
Cumulative frequencies	5	16	52	60

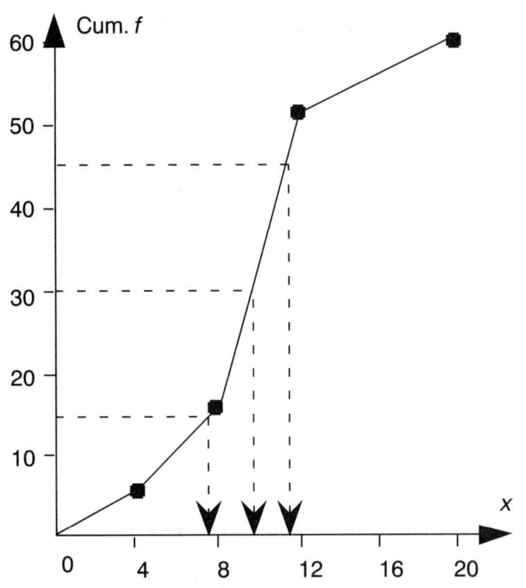

∴ Median = 9.6

Also $Q_1 = 7.6$ and $Q_3 = 11.2$

∴ Semi-interquartile range $= \frac{Q_3 - Q_1}{2}$

$= \frac{11.2 - 7.6}{2} = 1.8$

(c) $\bar{x} = 9.4$ and $s = 3.5646$

10

Ends	4.5	7.5	10.5	13.5
Cumulative frequencies	3	10	22	24

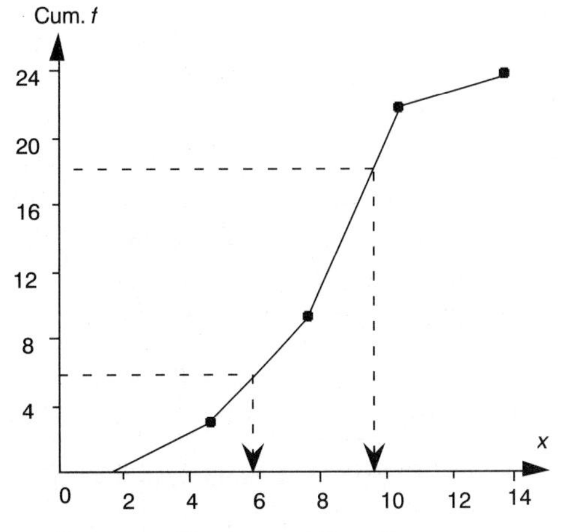

Interquartile range $= Q_3 - Q_1$

$= 9.5 - 5.8 = 3.7$

Section 5

1

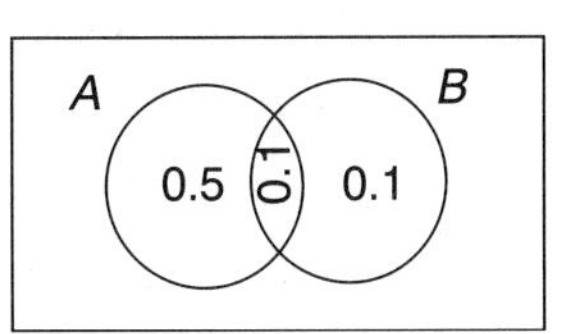

(a) $P(A' \cap B) = 0.1$

(b) P(A or B but not both) = 0.5 + 0.1 = 0.6

2 At least one Head $= \frac{7}{8}$

Score of more than 4 $= \frac{2}{6}$

Independent $\Rightarrow \frac{7}{8} \times \frac{2}{6} = \frac{7}{24}$

3 $3R$, $4W$, $5B$

(a) possibilities are RRR or WWW or BBB

P(all same colour)

$= \left(\frac{3}{12}\right)^3 + \left(\frac{4}{12}\right)^3 + \left(\frac{5}{12}\right)^3$

$= 0.125 = \frac{1}{8}$

(b) possibilities areRWB or RBW or BRW or BWR or WBR or WRB.

P(all different)$= \frac{3}{12} \times \frac{4}{11} \times \frac{5}{10} +$ 5 terms with the same numbers

$= 6 \times \frac{3}{12} \times \frac{4}{11} \times \frac{5}{10} = \frac{3}{11}$

4

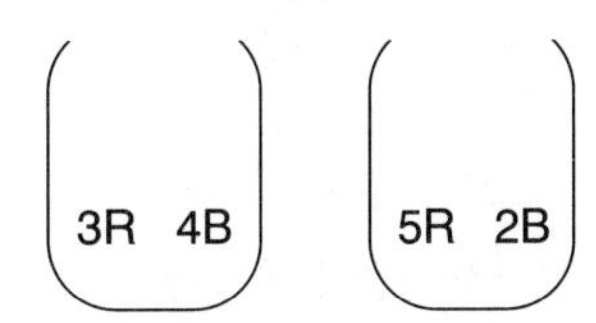

After transfer container 1 could be

$2R$ $4B$ with probability $\frac{3}{7}$

or $3R$ $3B$ with probability $\frac{4}{7}$

P(red selected from 1 after transfer)

$= \frac{3}{7} \times \frac{2}{6} + \frac{4}{7} \times \frac{3}{6} = \frac{3}{7}$

5 Number of permutations of 3 out of 5

$= {}^5P_3 = \frac{5!}{2!} = 60$

Looking at the ratio of odds to evens in the list $\frac{3}{5} \times 60$ will be odd

$= 36$

6 $4F\ 2M$

Committee consists of 1 male, 2 females

1 male can be selected in 2 ways

2 females can be selected in ${}^4C_2 = 6$ ways

Hence $2 \times 6 = 12$ committees

7 $3Y, 5G, 4R$

(a) possibilities are GG, RR, GR, RG

P(no yellows in 1st two)

$= \frac{5}{12} \times \frac{4}{11} + \frac{4}{12} \times \frac{3}{11}$

$+ \frac{5}{12} \times \frac{4}{11} + \frac{4}{12} \times \frac{5}{11}$

$= \frac{72}{132} = \frac{6}{11}$

(b) Possibilities are YY, YR, RY, YG, GY

which is the complement of (a) hence $\frac{5}{11}$

(c) Let A = 'fourth sweet is yellow'

B = 'first two sweets are red'

then $P(A \mid B) = \frac{P(A \cap B)}{P(B)}$

$A \cap B$ is $RRYY$ or $RRRY$ or $RRGY$

$$P(A \cap B) = \left(\frac{4}{12} \times \frac{3}{11} \times \frac{3}{10} \times \frac{2}{9}\right) + \left(\frac{4}{12} \times \frac{3}{11} \times \frac{2}{10} \times \frac{3}{9}\right) + \left(\frac{4}{12} \times \frac{3}{11} \times \frac{5}{10} \times \frac{3}{9}\right)$$

$= \frac{3}{110}$

B is RR

$P(B) = \frac{4}{12} \times \frac{3}{11} = \frac{1}{11}$

$$P(A \mid B) = \frac{\frac{3}{110}}{\frac{1}{11}} = \frac{3}{110} \times \frac{11}{1} = \frac{3}{10}$$

8 $P(A \cup B) = P(A) + P(B) - P(A \cap B)$

$= P(A) + P(B) - P(A) \times P(B)$

since A, B are independent

$\Rightarrow \beta = \alpha + P(B) - (\alpha\, P(B))$

$\Rightarrow \beta - \alpha = P(B)\,(1 - \alpha)$

$\Rightarrow P(B) = \frac{\beta - \alpha}{1 - \alpha}$

9

$HB\ \frac{10}{100}$ $HL\ \frac{20}{100}$

$P(HB \cup HL) = \frac{25}{100}$

$P(HB \cup HL) = P(HB) + P(HL) - P(HB \cap HL)$

$\Rightarrow \frac{25}{100} = \frac{10}{100} + \frac{20}{100} - P(HB \cap HL)$

$\Rightarrow P(HB \cap HL) = \frac{5}{100} = \frac{1}{20}$

$$P(HL \mid HB) = \frac{P(HL \cap HB)}{P(HB)} = \frac{\frac{1}{20}}{\frac{10}{100}} = \frac{1}{2}$$

10 (a) $P(A \mid B) = \frac{P(A \cap B)}{P(B)}$

$= \frac{P(A)\,P(B)}{P(B)} = P(A)$

since A, B are independent

$\Rightarrow P(A \mid B) = 0.2$

(b) $P(A \cap B) = P(A)\,P(B)$

$= 0.2 \times 0.15 = 0.03$

(c) $P(A \cup B) = P(A) + P(B) - P(A \cap B)$

$= 0.2 + 0.15 - 0.03$

$= 0.32$

11 $P(A \text{ wins}) = \frac{2}{3}$

A wins 3 games or 4 games out of 4 games

is $4\left(\frac{2}{3}\right)^3\left(\frac{1}{3}\right) + \left(\frac{2}{3}\right)^4 = \frac{16}{27}$

12 Let M = mice

V = vole

R = rest

$P(M) = \frac{1}{2}$

$P(V) = \frac{1}{5}$

$P(R) = 1 - \frac{1}{2} - \frac{1}{5} = \frac{3}{10}$

A = Albert, B = Belinda, K = Khalid, P = Poon

$P(A) = \frac{20}{100}$ $P(B) = \frac{45}{100}$

$P(K) = \frac{10}{100}$ $P(P) = \frac{25}{100}$

(a) (i) $P(A \cap M) = P(A) . P(M)$ since independent

$= \frac{20}{100} \times \frac{1}{2} = \frac{1}{10}$

(ii) $P(A' \cap R) = \frac{80}{100} \times \frac{3}{10} = \frac{6}{25}$

(b) Using $P(M \mid B) = \frac{P(M \cap B)}{P(B)}$

we have $P(M \cap B) = P(B) . P(M \mid B)$

$= \frac{45}{100} \times \frac{1}{3} = \frac{3}{20}$

(c) $P(M \mid K) = \frac{P(M \cap K)}{P(K)}$

$= \frac{\frac{5}{100}}{\frac{10}{100}} = \frac{1}{2}$

(d) $P(M) = P(M \cap A) + P(M \cap B) + P(M \cap K) + P(M \cap P)$

$= \frac{1}{10} + \frac{3}{20} + \frac{5}{100} + \frac{2}{10} = \frac{1}{2}$

(e) $P(B \mid M) = \frac{P(B \cap M)}{P(M)} = \frac{\frac{15}{100}}{\frac{1}{2}} = \frac{3}{10}$

Section 6

1 Possible outcomes for X are 0, 1, 2, 3

$X = 0$ occurs in 1 way $\bar{R}\bar{R}\bar{R}$ with probability $\frac{5}{10} \times \frac{4}{9} \times \frac{3}{8}$

$X = 1$ occurs in 3 ways $R\bar{R}\bar{R}$ or $\bar{R}R\bar{R}$ or $\bar{R}\bar{R}R$ with probability $3 \times \frac{5}{10} \times \frac{5}{9} \times \frac{4}{8}$

$X = 2$ occurs in 3 ways $RR\bar{R}$ or $R\bar{R}R$ or $\bar{R}RR$ with probability $3 \times \frac{5}{10} \times \frac{4}{9} \times \frac{5}{8}$

$X = 3$ occurs in 1 way RRR with probability $\frac{5}{10} \times \frac{4}{9} \times \frac{3}{8}$

giving

x	0	1	2	3
$P(X = x)$	$\frac{60}{720}$	$\frac{300}{720}$	$\frac{300}{720}$	$\frac{60}{720}$

$P(X > 1) = \frac{300 + 60}{720} = \frac{1}{2}$

2 $P(X = 0) = P(TTT) = \frac{1}{2} \times \frac{1}{2} \times \frac{1}{2} = \frac{1}{8}$

$P(X = 1) = P(HTT \text{ or } THT \text{ or } TTH)$

$= 3 \times \frac{1}{2} \times \frac{1}{2} \times \frac{1}{2} = \frac{3}{8}$

$P(X = 2) = P(HHT \text{ or } HTH \text{ or } THH)$

$= 3 \times \frac{1}{2} \times \frac{1}{2} \times \frac{1}{2} = \frac{3}{8}$

$P(X = 3) = P(HHH) = \frac{1}{2} \times \frac{1}{2} \times \frac{1}{2} = \frac{1}{8}$

X can take the values 0, 1, 2, 3, so it is a discrete variable.

Also $\Sigma p_i = \frac{1}{8} + \frac{3}{8} + \frac{3}{8} + \frac{1}{8} = 1$,

so X satisfies the conditions of a discrete random variable.

3 We have $k + \frac{k}{2} + \frac{l}{3} + \frac{l}{4} = 1$

$\Rightarrow \frac{3k}{2} + \frac{7l}{12} = 1 \quad \Rightarrow 18k + 7l = 12 \qquad (1)$

$P(X \le 2) = 2P(X > 2)$

$\Rightarrow \frac{3k}{2} = 2 \times \frac{7l}{12} \quad \Rightarrow 9k = 7l \qquad (2)$

Substituting gives

$18k + 9k = 12$

$\Rightarrow 27k = 12 \Rightarrow k = \frac{4}{9}$

$P(X = 2) = \frac{2}{9}$

4 (a) $\int_0^{0.6} 10\,cx^2\,dx + \int_{0.6}^{1} 9c\,(1 - x)\,dx = 1$

$\Rightarrow \left[\frac{10cx^3}{3}\right]_0^{0.6} + \left[9cx - \frac{9cx^2}{2}\right]_{0.6}^{1} = 1$

$\Rightarrow \; 0.72c + 9c - 4.5c - 5.4c + 1.62c = 1$

$\Rightarrow \; 1.44c = 1 \Rightarrow c = \frac{25}{36}$

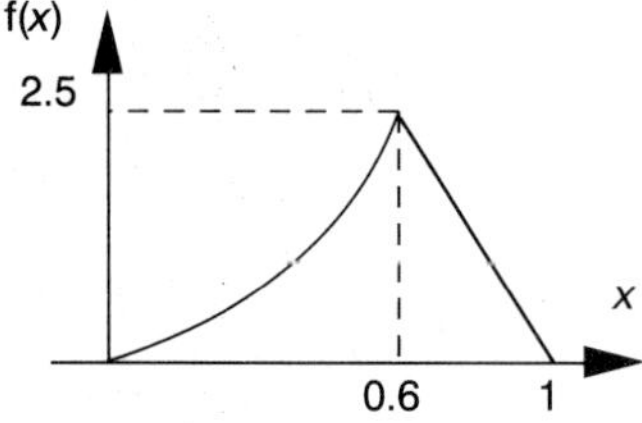

(b) Mode = 0.6

(c) $P(X < 0.4) = \int_0^{0.4} 10cx^2\,dx$

$= \left[\frac{10c\,x^3}{3}\right]_0^{0.4}$

$= \frac{10}{3} \times \frac{25}{36} \times 0.4^3 \;\; = 0.15$

5 $\int_0^1 6kx\,(1 - x)\,dx + \int_1^{\infty} \frac{k}{x^2}\,dx = 1$

$\Rightarrow 6k \int_0^1 (x - x^2)\,dx + k \int_1^{\infty} x^{-2}\,dx = 1$

$\Rightarrow 6k\left[\frac{x^2}{2} - \frac{x^3}{3}\right]_0^1 + k\left[\frac{-1}{x}\right]_1^{\infty} = 1$

$\Rightarrow 6k\left(\frac{1}{2} - \frac{1}{3}\right) + k\,(0 + 1) = 1$

$\Rightarrow k + k = 1 \;\; \Rightarrow k = \frac{1}{2}$

$P\left(X > \frac{1}{2}\right) = \int_{1/2}^{1} 6kx\,(1 - x)\,dx + \int_1^{\infty} \frac{k}{x^2}\,dx$

or more simply using the complement

$P\left(X > \frac{1}{2}\right) \;\; = 1 - P\left(X \le \frac{1}{2}\right)$

$= 1 - \int_0^{1/2} 6kx(1 - x)\,dx$

$= 1 - \int_0^{1/2} (3x - 3x^2)\,dx$

$= 1 - \left[\frac{3x^2}{2} - x^3\right]_0^{1/2} = \frac{3}{4}$

6 $F(x) \;\; = \int_0^x 3t(1 - t)\,dt$

$= \left[\frac{3t^2}{2} - t^3\right]_0^x$

$= \frac{3x^2}{2} - x^3$ for $0 < x < 1$

$F(x) \;\; = F(1) + \int_1^x \frac{1}{2t^2}\,dt$

$= \frac{1}{2} + \left[\frac{-1}{2t}\right]_1^x$

$= \frac{1}{2} + \left[\frac{-1}{2x} + \frac{1}{2}\right]$

$= 1 - \frac{1}{2x}$ for $x \ge 1$

Hence

$$F(x) = \begin{cases} 0 & x \le 0 \\ \frac{3x^2}{2} - x^3 & 0 < x \le 1 \\ 1 - \frac{1}{2x} & x \ge 1 \end{cases}$$

(a) $F\left(\frac{1}{2}\right) = \frac{3}{2}\left(\frac{1}{2}\right)^2 - \left(\frac{1}{2}\right)^3$

$= \frac{3}{8} - \frac{1}{8} = \frac{1}{4}$

(giving $P\left(X \le \frac{1}{2}\right) = \frac{1}{4}$ which concurs with answer to Exercise 4.)

$F(5) = 1 - \frac{1}{10} = \frac{9}{10}$

so $P(X \le 5) = \frac{9}{10}$

7 $f(x) = \dfrac{d}{dx}F(x)$

$$= \frac{d}{dx}\left[\frac{6}{1000}\left(5x^2 - \frac{1}{3}x^3\right)\right]$$

$$= \frac{6}{1000}(10x - x^2)$$

In full PDF is

$$f(x) = \begin{cases} 0 & x \le 0 \\ \dfrac{6}{1000}(10x - x^2) & 0 \le x \le 10 \\ 0 & x > 10 \end{cases}$$

The PDF of X:

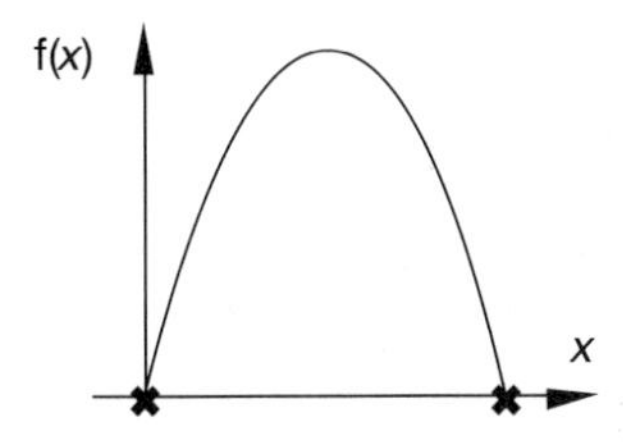

(b) P(Tube does not fail in first two years)

$$= P(X > 2) = 1 - P(X \le 2) = 1 - F(2)$$

$$= 1 - \frac{6}{1000}\left(20 - \frac{8}{3}\right) = \frac{112}{125}$$

For 8 tubes probability $= \left(\dfrac{112}{125}\right)^8 \sim 0.42$

(c) Let B = event 'tube lasts at least two years'. Then $P(B) = \dfrac{112}{125}$

and let A = event 'tube tasts at least four years'

then we require $P(A \mid B) = \dfrac{P(A \cap B)}{P(B)}$

$A \cap B$ is tube lasts two years and tube last four years which reduces to tube lasts 4 years.

$$P(X > 4) = 1 - P(X \le 4) = 1 - F(4) = \frac{648}{1000}$$

$$\text{Hence } P(A \mid B) = \frac{\frac{648}{1000}}{\frac{896}{1000}} = \frac{648}{896} = \frac{81}{112}$$

(d) No tube can last more than 10 years. Unlikely to be a symmetrical distribution – more likely to have a positive skew.

8 $E(X) = 0 \times \frac{1}{8} + 1 \times \frac{3}{8} + 2 \times \frac{3}{8} + 3 \times \frac{1}{8}$

$$= \frac{12}{8} = 1.5$$

$E(X^2) = 0^2 \times \frac{1}{8} + 1^2 \times \frac{3}{8} + 2^2 \times \frac{3}{8} + 3^2 \times \frac{1}{8}$

$$= \frac{24}{8} = 3$$

$\text{Var}(X) = 3 - \left(\frac{3}{2}\right)^2 = \frac{3}{4}$

9 (a) $p(1) = k$

$p(2) = 4k$

$p(3) = 9k$

$9k + 4k + k = 1 \Rightarrow k = \dfrac{1}{14}$

(b) $E(X) = 1 \times \dfrac{1}{14} + 2 \times \dfrac{4}{14} + 3 \times \dfrac{9}{14}$

$$= \frac{36}{14} = \frac{18}{7}$$

(c) $E(X^2) = 1^2 \times \dfrac{1}{14} + 2^2 \times \dfrac{4}{14} + 3^2 \times \dfrac{9}{14} = \dfrac{98}{14}$

$\text{Var}(X) = \dfrac{98}{14} - \left(\dfrac{18}{7}\right)^2 = 0.388$

10

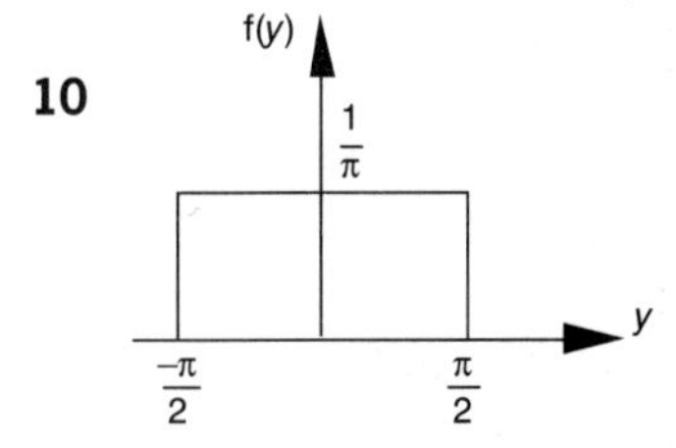

(a) $E(Y) = 0$ (by symmetry)

(b) $E(Y^2) = \displaystyle\int_{-\pi/2}^{\pi/2} y^2 . \frac{1}{\pi}\,dy = \frac{\pi^2}{12}$

$\text{Var}(Y) = \dfrac{\pi^2}{12} - 0^2 = \dfrac{\pi^2}{12}$

11 (a) $\displaystyle\int_{-\infty}^{\infty} f(x)\,dx = \int_1^2 k(x^2 + 2x)\,dx$

$$= k\left[\frac{x^3}{3} + x^2\right]_1^2 = \frac{16k}{3}$$

Since this must be one, we have $k = \dfrac{3}{16}$

(b) $E(X) = \frac{3}{16}\int_1^2 (x^3 + 2x^2)\,dx$

$= \frac{3}{16}\left[\frac{x^4}{4} + \frac{2x^3}{3}\right]_1^2$

$= \frac{101}{64} = 1.58$ (2 d.p.)

$E(X^2) = \frac{3}{16}\int_1^2 (x^4 + 2x^3)\,dx = \frac{411}{160}$

$Var(X) = \frac{411}{160} - \left(\frac{101}{64}\right)^2$

$= 0.08$ (2 d.p.)

12 (a) $\int_0^2 kx(2-x)\,dx = 1$

$\Rightarrow k\left[x^2 - \frac{x^3}{3}\right]_0^2 = 1$

$\Rightarrow k\frac{4}{3} = 1 \quad \Rightarrow k = \frac{3}{4}$

(b) Mode = 1

(c) Median = 1

both by symmetry (or calculus)

13 (a) $E(5X + 7) = 5E(X) + 7$
$= 5 \times 20 + 7 = 107$

(b) $Var(5X + 7) = Var(5X)$
$= 5^2Var(X) = 25 \times 2 = 50$

(c) $E(5X + 7Y) = 5E(X) + 7E(Y)$
$= 5 \times 20 + 7 \times 24 = 268$

(d) $Var(5X + 7Y) = 5^2Var(X) + 7^2Var(Y)$
$= 5^2 \times 2 + 7^2 \times 3 = 197$

(e) $E(5X - 7Y) = 5E(X) - 7E(Y)$
$= 5 \times 20 - 7 \times 24 = -68$

(f) $Var(5X - 7Y) = 5^2Var(X) + 7^2Var(Y)$
$= 5^2 \times 2 + 7^2 \times 3 = 197$
(Note this + sign ↑)

(g) $E(5 - 7Y) = 5 - 7E(Y)$
$= 5 - 7 \times 24 = -163$

(h) $Var(5 - 7Y) = Var(-7Y)$
$= 7^2Var(Y) = 7^2 \times 3 = 147$

14 (a) $p(1) = k$

$p(2) = 8k$

$p(3) = 27k$

$p(4) = 64k$

$k + 8k + 27k + 64k = 100k = 1$

$\Rightarrow k = \frac{1}{100}$

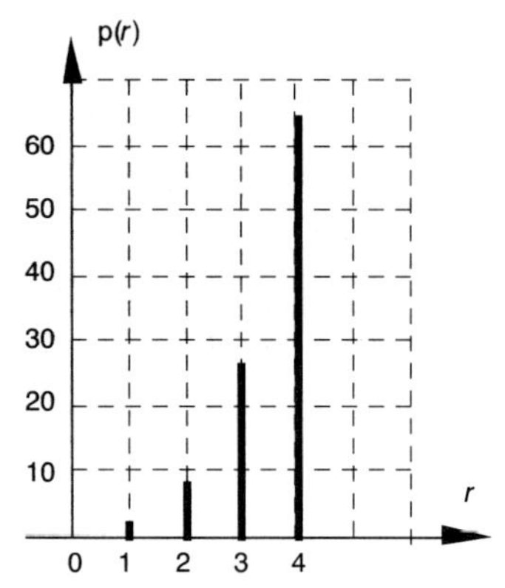

(b) $E(R) = 1 \times \frac{1}{100} + 2 \times \frac{8}{100} + 3 \times \frac{27}{100} + 4 \times \frac{64}{100}$

$= \frac{354}{100} = 3.54$

$E(R^2) = 1^2 \times \frac{1}{100} + 2^2 \times \frac{8}{100} + 3^2 \times \frac{27}{100} + 4^2 \times \frac{64}{100}$

$= \frac{1300}{100} = 13$

$\Rightarrow Var(R) = 13 - 3.54^2 = 0.4684$

(c) $E(5R - 3) = 5E(R) - 3 = 14.7$

$Var(5R - 3) = 25Var(R) = 11.71$

15 (a) $3X$ has distribution

r	0	3	6
$P(3X = r)$	$\frac{1}{3}$	$\frac{1}{2}$	$\frac{1}{6}$

(b) $2Y$ has distribution

r	-2	2
$P(2Y = r)$	$\frac{3}{4}$	$\frac{1}{4}$

(c) $3X + 2Y$ has the distribution

r	-2	1	2	4	5	8
$P(3X + 2Y = r)$	$\frac{6}{24}$	$\frac{9}{24}$	$\frac{2}{24}$	$\frac{3}{24}$	$\frac{3}{24}$	$\frac{1}{24}$

(d) $E(X) = 0 \times \frac{1}{3} + 1 \times \frac{1}{2} + 2 \times \frac{1}{6} = \frac{5}{6}$

$E(X^2) = 0 \times \frac{1}{3} + 1^2 \times \frac{1}{2} + 2^2 \times \frac{1}{6} = \frac{7}{6}$

$\Rightarrow \text{Var}(X) = \frac{7}{6} - \left(\frac{5}{6}\right)^2 = \frac{17}{36}$

(e) $E(Y) = (-1) \times \frac{3}{4} + 1 \times \frac{1}{4} = \frac{-1}{2}$

$E(Y^2) = 1 \times \frac{3}{4} + 1 \times \frac{1}{4} = 1$

$\text{Var}(Y) = 1 - \left(\frac{-1}{2}\right)^2 = \frac{3}{4}$

(f) $E(3X + 2Y) = \frac{36}{24}$

$E\left((3X + 2Y)^2\right) = \frac{228}{24}$

$\text{Var}(3X + 2Y) = \frac{29}{4}$

Section 7

1

r	1	2	3	...	n
$P(X = 6)$	$\frac{1}{n}$	$\frac{1}{n}$	$\frac{1}{n}$		$\frac{1}{n}$

$$E(X) = 1 \times \frac{1}{n} + 2 \times \frac{1}{n} + 3 \times \frac{1}{n} + \ldots + n \times \frac{1}{n}$$
$$= \frac{1}{n}(1 + 2 + 3 + \ldots + n)$$
$$= \frac{1}{n} \cdot \frac{1}{2} n(n+1) = \frac{n+1}{2}$$

$$E(X^2) = 1^2 \times \frac{1}{n} + 2^2 \times \frac{1}{n} + 3^2 \times \frac{1}{n} + \ldots + n^2 \times \frac{1}{n}$$
$$= \frac{1}{n}[1^2 + 2^2 + 3^2 + \ldots + n^2]$$
$$= \frac{1}{n} \cdot \frac{1}{6} n(n+1)(2n+1)$$
$$= \frac{1}{6}(n+1)(2n+1)$$

$$\text{Var}(X) = \frac{1}{6}(n+1)(2n+1) - \frac{(n+1)^2}{4}$$
$$= \frac{n+1}{24}\left(4(2n+1) - 6(n+1)\right)$$
$$= \frac{n+1}{24}(2n-2) = \frac{(n+1)(n-1)}{12}$$

$$P(X > m) = 1 - P(X \le m)$$
$$= 1 - \underbrace{\left[\frac{1}{n} + \frac{1}{n} + \frac{1}{n} + \ldots + \frac{1}{n}\right]}_{m \text{ times}}$$
$$= 1 - \frac{m}{n}$$

2 $X \sim B(10, 0.15)$

$$P(X \ge 4) = 1 - P(X \le 3)$$
$$= 1 - [P(X = 0) + P(X = 1) + P(X = 2) + P(X = 3)]$$
$$= 1 - [(0.85)^{10} + 10(0.85)^9(0.15) + 45(0.85)^8(0.15)^2 + 120(0.85)^7(0.15)^3]$$
$$= 0.05$$

$E(X) = 10 \times 0.15 = 1.5$

$P(X > 1.5) = P(X \geq 2) = 1 - P(X \leq 1)$

$= 1 - (0.85)^{10} - 10(0.85)^9(0.15) = 0.46$

3 (a) $X \sim B(5, 0.35)$

$P(X = 0) = (0.65)^5 = 0.1160$

$P(X = 1) = 5 \times 0.35 \times 0.65^4 = 0.3124$

$P(X = 2) = {}^5C_2 \times 0.35^2 \times 0.65^3 = 0.3364$

$P(X = 3) = {}^5C_3 \times 0.35^3 \times 0.65^2 = 0.1811$

$P(X = 4) = 5 \times 0.35^4 \times 0.65 = 0.0488$

$P(X = 5) = 0.35^5 = 0.0053$

$E(X) = 5 \times 0.35 = 1.75$

$Var(X) = 1.75 \times 0.65 = 1.1375$

(b) We need $np = 1$,

i.e. $5p = 1$, so that $p = 0.2$

Then $P(X > 1) = 1 - P(X = 0) - P(X = 1)$

$= 1 - 0.8^5 - 5 \times 0.8^4 \times 0.2 = 0.26272$

4 Let n = number of throws required. Then the distribution of X the number of hits is $X \sim B(n, 0.4)$

For this distribution we require

$P(X \geq 1) \geq 0.9$

$\Rightarrow P(X < 1) \leq 0.1$

$\Rightarrow P(X = 0) \leq 0.1$

$\Rightarrow (0.6)^n \leq 0.1$

$\Rightarrow n \log(0.6) \leq \log(0.1)$

$\Rightarrow n \geq \frac{\log 0.1}{\log 0.6} = 4.508$

$\Rightarrow n = 5$

5 We must use the block of the table for $n = 10$ and, in that block, find the column for $p = 0.2$.

(a) As the heading of the table makes clear, the figures are for 'less than or equal to' probabilities, so $P(X \leq 3)$ is found by a straightforward reading of the $x = 3$ row, giving 0.8791.

(b) Other probabilities need to be transformed into 'less than or equal to' language.

So $P(X > 6) = 1 - P(X \leq 6)$

$= 1 - 0.9991 = 0.0009$

(c) $P(4 \leq X < 8) = P(3 < X \leq 7)$

$= P(X \leq 7) - P(X \leq 3)$

$= 0.9999 - 0.8791 = 0.1208$

6 You will notice that the tables only go up to $p = 0.5$. We must therefore perform a reflection of the distribution, reversing the roles of p and q. So we shall use the $n = 10$ block of the table and the $p = 0.2$ column.

Then $P(X \leq 3)$ when $p = 0.8$

$= P(X \geq 7)$ when $p = 0.2$

$= 1 - P(X \leq 6) = 1 - 0.9991 = 0.0009$

7 Let X = number sold per week

then $X \sim P(4)$

(a) $P(X \geq 2) = 1 - P(X = 0) - P(X = 1)$

$= 1 - e^{-4} - 4e^{-4}$

$= 0.91$

(b) Keep adding up

$P(X = 0) + P(X = 1) + \ldots$

until 0.99 at least is obtained.

So need to make

$$e^{-4}\left[1 + 4 + \frac{4^2}{2!} + \frac{4^3}{3!} + \frac{4^4}{4!} + \ldots\right] > 0.99$$

i.e. need

$$\left[1 + 4 + \frac{4^2}{2!} + \frac{4^3}{3!} + \frac{4^4}{4!} + \ldots\right] > 54.0522$$

By trial and error 9 radios should be held.

(c) Sales are random in time although may be affected by advertising campaigns and seasonal factors.

8 X = number of accidents per week

$X \sim P(2.5)$

(a) $P(X = 5) = \frac{2.5^5 e^{-2.5}}{5!} = 0.067$

(b) If Y is the number of accidents in 4 weeks, then $Y \sim P(10)$

require $P(Y > 14) = 1 - P(Y \leq 14)$

$= 0.083$

9 $X \sim B(35, 0.1)$

$\Rightarrow X \approx P(3.5)$

$$P(X \leq 5) \approx e^{-3.5}\left[1 + 3.5 + \frac{3.5^2}{2!} + \frac{3.5^3}{3!} + \frac{3.5^4}{4!} + \frac{3.5^5}{5!}\right]$$

≈ 0.858

10 (a) Derivations given in Section 7, pp. 120–21.

(b) (i) Expected income = $2.6 \times 5 = £13$

(ii) Vacuum cleaners demanded per day X is $X \sim P(2.6)$

(a) $P(X = 0) = e^{-2.6} = 0.0743$

(b) $P(X = 1) = 2.6e^{-2.6} = 0.1931$

(c) $P(X = 2) = \dfrac{2.6^2\, e^{-2.6}}{2!} = 0.2510$

(d) $P(X \geq 3) =$
$1 - 0.0743 - 0.1931 - 0.2510$
$= 0.4816$

(iii) Mean daily income

$= 0 \times 0.0743 \times 5 + 1 \times 0.1931 \times 5$

$+ 2 \times 0.2510 \times 5$

$+ 3 \times \dfrac{2.6^3 \times e^{-2.6}}{3!} \times 5$

$= 5\,[0.1931 + 0.502 + 0.6527]$

$= £6.74$

Extra income available by hiring more than 3 vacuum cleaners is

$$£5 \times \left(1 - e^{-2.6} - 2.6e^{-2.6} - \frac{2.6^2 e^{-2.6}}{2} - \frac{2.6^3 e^{-2.6}}{6}\right)$$

$= £1.32$

Hence shopkeeper should not take up offer.

11 For Poisson with mean 3.5, we find the $\mu = 3.5$ column and read off 'less than or equal to' probabilities against the appropriate values of x.

(a) $P(X \leq 10) = 0.9990$

(b) $P(X \geq 8) = 1 - P(X < 8) = 1 - P(X \leq 7)$
$= 1 - 0.9733 = 0.0267$

(c) $P(5 \leq X < 11) = P(X \leq 10) - P(X \leq 4)$
$= 0.9990 - 0.7254 = 0.2736$

Section 8

1 $E(X) = \dfrac{3 + (-1)}{2} = 1$

$\text{Var}(X) = \dfrac{(3 - (-1))^2}{12} = \dfrac{4}{3}$

$P(X > 0) = \dfrac{3}{4}$

$F(x) = \dfrac{x - (-1)}{3 - (-1)} = \dfrac{x + 1}{4}$

In full

$$F(x) = \begin{cases} 0 & x < -1 \\ \dfrac{x+1}{4} & 1 \leq x \leq 3 \\ 1 & x > 3 \end{cases}$$

PDF of X

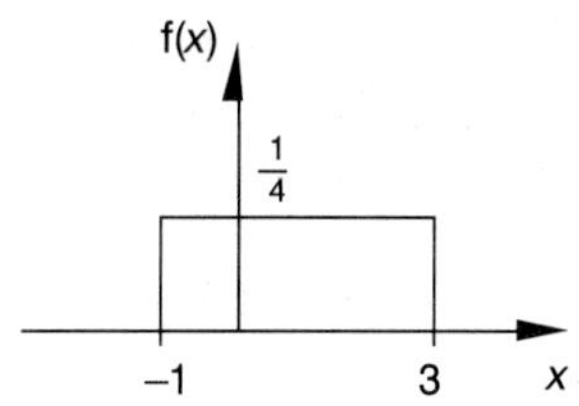

CDF of X

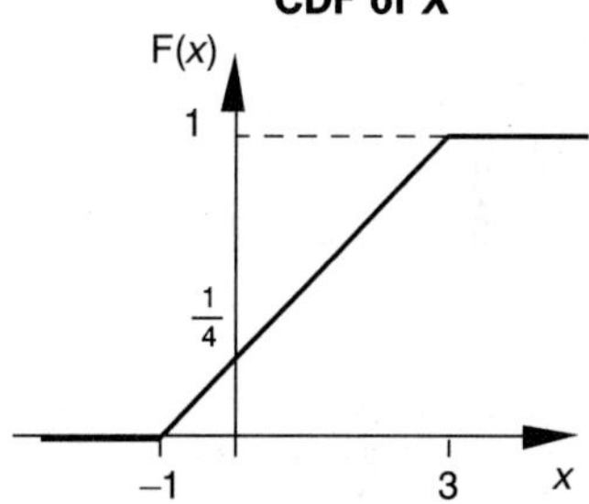

2 (a) $z = \dfrac{87 - 80}{4} = 1.75$

Ans: 0.9599 (or 95.99%)

(b) $z = \dfrac{86 - 80}{4} = 1.5$

Ans: 0.0668 (or 6.68%)

(c) $z_1 = \dfrac{75 - 80}{4} = -1.25$
which gives 0.8944

$z_2 = \dfrac{78 - 80}{4} = -0.5$
which gives 0.6915

Subtract these areas to get
Ans: 0.2029 (or 20.29%)

(d) $z_1 = \frac{85.5 - 80}{4} = 1.375$

which gives 0.9154

$z_2 = \frac{77 - 80}{4} = -0.75$

which gives 0.7734

$\therefore$ required area = 0.4154 + 0.2734
= 0.6888 (or 68.88%)

(e) $z = \frac{82 - 80}{3} = 0.667$

Now 0.66 gives 0.7454

and 0.67 gives 0.7486

$\therefore$ 0.667 gives 0.7476

(We want $\frac{7}{10}$ of the way along between 54 and 86.

Now 86 – 54 = 32 and

$\frac{7}{10} \times 32 = 22$ (approx)

$\therefore$ We want 54 + 22 = 76.)

$\therefore$ Ans: 0.2476 (or 24.76%)

(f) $z = \frac{87 - 80}{6} = 1.167$

Now 1.16 gives 0.8770

and 1.17 gives 0.8790

$\therefore$ 1.167 gives 0.8784

$\therefore$ Ans: 0.1216 (or 12.16%)

3 (a) $\frac{x - 80}{4} = 1.175 \quad \therefore x = 84.7$

(b) $\frac{x - 80}{4} = -0.44$ (note negative sign)

$\therefore x = 78.24$

(c) $\frac{x - 80}{4} = 0.841 \quad \therefore x = 83.36$

(d) $\frac{x - 80}{4} = -1.037 \quad \therefore x = 75.85$

4 (a) Let $Z = \frac{X - \mu}{5}$ then $Z \sim N(0,1)$

$P(X < 32) = P\left(Z < \frac{32 - \mu}{5}\right) = 0.6$

From tables

$P(Z < 0.26) = 0.603$ (the nearest)

Hence comparing these $\frac{32 - \mu}{5} = 0.26$

and solving gives $\mu = 30.7$

(b) Let $Z = \frac{X - 40}{\sigma}$ then $Z \sim N(0,1)$

$P(X > 37) = P\left(Z > -\frac{3}{\sigma}\right)$

$= P\left(Z < \frac{3}{\sigma}\right)$ (by symmetry)

$= 0.7$

The symmetry can be checked by sketching the areas:

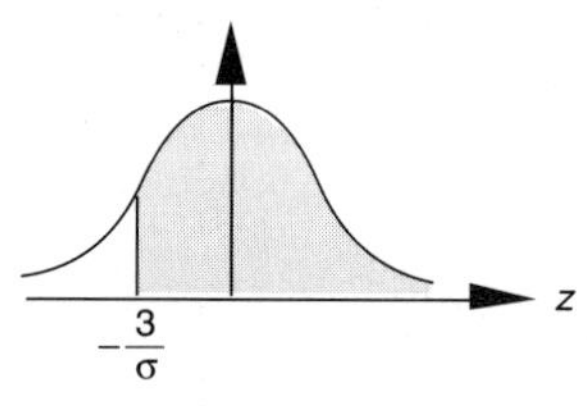

is clearly the same area as

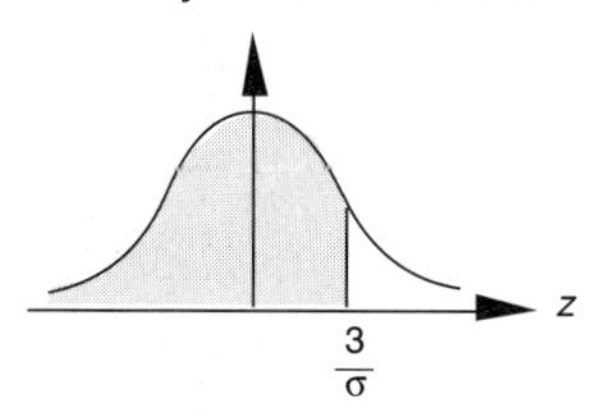

From tables

$P(Z > 0.53) = 0.702$ (the nearest entry)

and comparing gives $\frac{3}{\sigma} = 0.53$

$\Rightarrow \quad \sigma = 5.66$

(c) Let $Z = \frac{X - \mu}{\sigma}$ then $Z \sim N(0,1)$

$P(X < 22) = P\left(Z < \frac{22 - \mu}{\sigma}\right) = 0.74$

and since $P(Z < 0.64) \approx 0.74$

we have $\frac{22 - \mu}{\sigma} = 0.64$

or $\quad 22 - \mu = 0.64\sigma \qquad [1]$

$P(X > 17) = P\left(Z > \frac{17 - \mu}{\sigma}\right) = 0.78$

and since $P(Z > -0.77) = 0.78$

we have $\frac{17 - \mu}{\sigma} = -0.77$

$\Rightarrow \quad 17 - \mu = -0.77\sigma \qquad [2]$

$[1] - [2] \Rightarrow 5 = 1.41\sigma \quad \Rightarrow \sigma = 3.55$

$\Rightarrow \quad \sigma^2 = 12.6$

Substituting into [1] gives $\mu = 22 - 2.27$

$\Rightarrow \mu = 19.7$

5 $X \sim B(200, 0.45)$

$\Rightarrow X \approx N(90, 49.5)$

(a) $P(X \leq 76) \approx P(X \leq 76.5)$
(using continuity correction)

Let $Z = \dfrac{X - 90}{7.04}$

then $P(X \leq 76.5) = P(Z \leq -1.92)$

$= 1 - P(Z \leq 1.92)$

$= 1 - 0.973 \quad = 0.03$ (2 d.p.)

(b) $P(X > 110) = 1 - P(X \leq 110)$

$\approx 1 - P(X \leq 110.5)$
(continuity correction)

$P(X \leq 110.5) \approx P(Z \leq 2.91) = 0.998$

so $P(X > 110) = 0.002$

(c) $P(80 \leq X < 100)$

$= P(X \leq 99) - P(X \leq 79)$

$\approx P(X \leq 99.5) - P(X \leq 79.5)$
(by continuity correction)

$= P(Z \leq 1.349) - P(Z \leq -1.492)$

$= P(Z \leq 1.349) - (1 - P(Z \leq 1.492))$

$= 0.912 - (1 - 0.932) = 0.844$

6 (a) P(more than 3) = P(4 or 5 or 6 or 7)

$= \dfrac{7!}{4!3!}(0.4)^4(0.6)^3 + \dfrac{7!}{5!2!}(0.4)^5(0.6)^2$

$+ \dfrac{7!}{6!1!}(0.4)^6(0.6) + (0.4)^7$

$= 0.290$

(b) $n = 700, p = 0.4$

$\therefore$ Mean $= np = 700 \times 0.4 = 280$

And Variance $= np(1 - p)$

$= 700 \times 0.4 \times 0.6 = 168 \qquad \therefore \sigma = \sqrt{168}$

More than 300 means we need the shaded area in the following diagram:

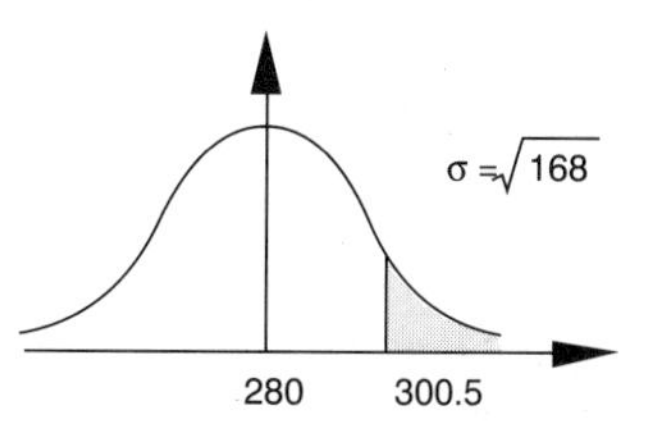

Now $Z = \dfrac{300.5 - 280}{\sqrt{168}} = 1.582$

The standard normal tables give 0.9431

$\therefore$ Ans = 0.0569

7 (a) $\therefore P(0 \text{ error}) = 1 - \dfrac{3}{10\,000} = 0.9997$

$\therefore P(0 \text{ errors in } 5000) = 0.9997^{5000} = 0.223$

(b) mean = 300 $\therefore$ Variance = 300

$\therefore \sigma = \sqrt{300}$

No more than 280 means that we need the shaded area below:

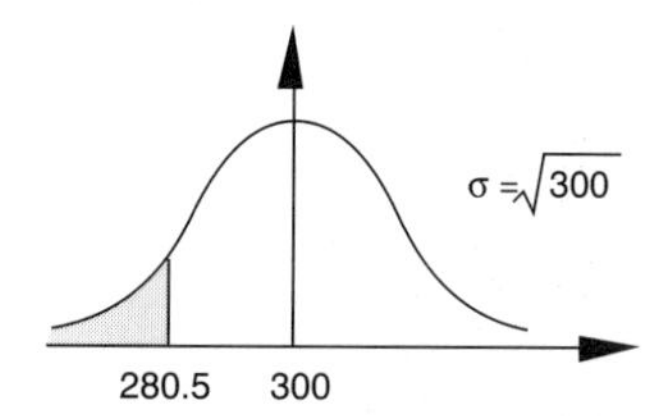

Now $Z = \dfrac{280 - 300}{\sqrt{300}} = -1.155$

The standard normal tables give 0.8759

$\therefore$ Ans: 0.124

8 (a) $X \sim U(3,9)$

$E(X) = 6$

$\text{Var}(X) = \dfrac{(9-3)^2}{12} = 3$

(b) $\bar{x} = \dfrac{590}{100} = 5.9$

$s^2 = \dfrac{3571}{100} - 5.9^2 = 0.9$

(c) Although the means are close the variances vary considerably. The data is much less spread out than the model predicted.

(d) $X \sim N(\mu,\sigma^2)$

$P(X < 4.3) = \frac{5}{100} = 0.05$

$P(X > 6.9) = \frac{17}{100} = 0.17$

Let $Z = \frac{X-\mu}{\sigma}$ then $Z \sim N(0,1)$

$P(X < 4.3) = P\left(Z < \frac{4.3-\mu}{\sigma}\right) = 0.05$

But from tables

$P(Z < -1.65) = 0.05$

$\Rightarrow \frac{4.3-\mu}{\sigma} = -1.65$

$\Rightarrow 4.3 - \mu = -1.65\sigma$ [1]

$P(X > 6.9) = P\left(Z > \frac{6.9-\mu}{\sigma}\right) = 0.17$

But from tables $P(Z > 0.95) = 0.17$

$\Rightarrow \frac{6.9-\mu}{\sigma} = 0.95$

$\Rightarrow 6.9 - \mu = 0.95\sigma$ [2]

Solving [1] and [2] simultaneously gives

$6.9 - 4.3 = 0.95\sigma + 1.65\sigma$

$\Rightarrow \sigma = 1$

$\Rightarrow \mu = 5.95$

(e) Mean and variance are much closer to actual data suggesting normal is better model.

9 (a) $X \sim N(1000,12^2)$

$P(X < 985) = 0.106$

(b) $X \sim N(\mu,12^2)$

$P(X < 1000) = 0.01$

$\Rightarrow \mu = 1.03$ kg

10 (a) (i) $X \sim N(19,3^2)$

$P(X < 15) = 0.09$

(ii) $P(X > x) = 0.1$

$\Rightarrow x = 22.9$ minutes

(b) $Y \sim N(\mu,7^2)$

$P(Y > 8) = 0.97725$

$\Rightarrow \mu = 22$ minutes

(c) $T = Y - X$ has

$T \sim N(22 - 19, 3^2 + 7^2)$

i.e. $T \sim N(3,58)$

Toto's first if $X < Y$

i.e. if $Y - X > 0$

$P(Y - X > 0) = P(T > 0)$

$= 0.653$

(d) For Toto's $P(X < 10)$

$= P(Z < -3)$

$\approx$ very small

For Blue Star $P(Y < 10)$

$= P(Z < -1.7)$

≈ 0.04

Very small probability of catching train but better than Toto's.

Appendix 1: Summary of basic set theory

For those students unfamiliar with the fundamental ideas and concepts of set theory, these are summarised below.

Elements of sets

A set is a collection of objects with some property in common and is a well-defined entity, in the sense that it is possible to say unambiguously whether something is in the set or not.

For example:

$A = \{\text{ the set of prime numbers less than 30 }\}$

is a well-defined collection of positive integers, and, for example:

$$7 \in A \qquad 39 \notin A \qquad 68.4 \notin A$$

where the symbol $\in$ means 'is a member of' or 'is an element of' and $\notin$ means the negation of this, i.e. 'is not a member of'.

Sets are placed in curly brackets conventionally, as in the example above. They may be defined by a property, as in A above, or they may be defined by a list. For example:

$$B = \{ 1, 2, 3, 4, 5, 6 \}$$

is the set of outcomes for an ordinary cubical die.

Sets may have an infinite number of members, e.g.

$\mathbb{Z}$, the **set of integers**

or $\mathbb{R}$ the **set of real numbers**.

All x { x : }

An alternative way in which sets may be defined by a rule is as in the example:

$$C = \{ x : x \in \mathbb{Z}, x > \sqrt{3})$$

which should be read as:

'all x such that x is an integer ($\in \mathbb{Z}$) and x is bigger than $\sqrt{3}$.'

This could equivalently be defined by the list:

$$C = \{ 2, 3, 4, \ldots \}$$

where the ... has an obvious meaning.

n(X)

The notation n(X) means the **number of elements** or objects in X and from the above examples:

n(A) = 10

since $A = \{ 2, 3, 5, 7, 11, 13, 17, 19, 23, 29 \}$

n(B) = 6

n(C) is infinite

Subsets

An important relationship between sets is that of a **subset**:

$X \subset Y$ (read as 'X is a subset of Y')

if everything in X is also in Y. So, for example:

if $A = \{ 1, 2, 3 \}$

and $B = \{ 4, 1, 2, 3, \}$

then $A \subset B$

but $B \not\subset A$ i.e. B is not a subset of A.

For some sets that you may have met in pure maths, the following relationships hold:

$$\mathbb{N} \subset \mathbb{Z} \subset \mathbb{R} \subset \mathbb{C}$$

i.e. natural numbers are included in integers which are included in real numbers which are included in complex numbers.

Note that according to the definition,

$$X \subset X \text{ always}$$

since everything in X is automatically in X, and

$$\varnothing \subset X$$

since there are no things in $\varnothing$ which could not be in X.

The universal set $\mathscr{E}$

Any discussion or argument usually takes place within a context and in set theory, the context is called the universal set ($\mathscr{E}$). Once the universal set has been fixed, then all subsequent discussion takes place within that context. The universal set is analagous to the sample space.

An an example, suppose:

$$\mathscr{E} = \{ \text{positive integers} \}$$

and $A = \{ \text{prime numbers} \}$

then we can define a new set, the **complement** of A written A' which is everything in $\mathscr{E}$ but not in A, which in this case will be non-prime (or composite) positive integers. For example:

$$7 \in A$$

and $18 \in A'$

Note, however, that $25.2 \notin A'$ as we had already confined the discussion to positive integers by defining $\mathscr{E}$.

Intersection of sets

The intersection of two sets A and B, written $A \cap B$ is defined formally by:

$$\{ x : x \in A \text{ and } x \in B \}$$

and so is the set of those things in common to both A and B.

Union of sets

The union of two sets A and B is written $A \cup B$ and is formally defined by:

$$\{ x : x \in A \text{ or } x \in B \}$$

and so is the set of those things which are either in A or B, or both.

Venn diagrams

The complement, union and intersection of sets can be neatly illustrated using **Venn Diagrams**. Conventionally the universal set is a rectangle and then sets within it are circles.

As an example consider:

$$\mathscr{E} = \{ 1, 2, 3, 4, 5, 6, 7, 8 \}$$

$$A = \{ 2, 4, 6, 8 \}$$

$$B = \{ 3, 4, 5, 6 \}$$

then the sets can be illustrated as follows:

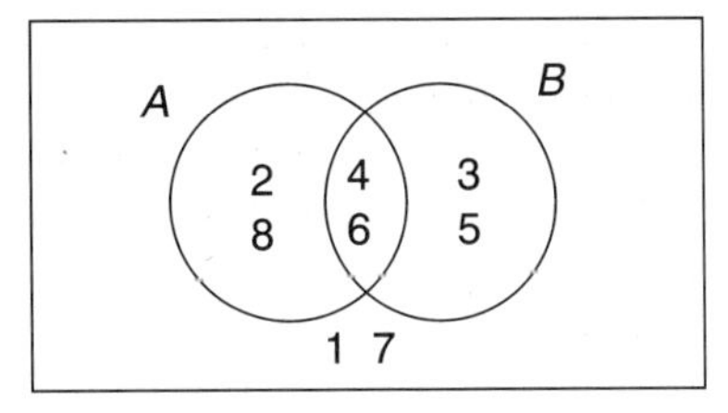

and it is clear from the diagram that for example:

$$A \cap B = \{ 4, 6 \}$$

$$A \cup B = \{ 2, 3, 4, 5, 6, 8 \}$$

$$A' = \{ 1, 7, 3, 5 \}$$

$$\text{n}(B') = 4$$

$$(A \cap B)' = \{ 2, 8, 3, 5, 1, 7 \}$$

$$(A \cap B) \subset A$$

Sets and set notation are widely used in probability theory and Venn Diagrams provide a useful problem-solving tool.

Appendix 2: The normal distribution function

The function tabulated below is $\Phi(z)$, defined as $\Phi(z) = \dfrac{1}{\sqrt{2\pi}} \displaystyle\int_{-\infty}^{z} e^{-\frac{1}{2}t^2}\, dt$.

z	$\Phi(z)$	z	$\Phi(z)$	z	$\Phi(z)$	z	$\Phi(z)$	z	$\Phi(z)$
0.00	0.5000	0.50	0.6915	1.00	0.8413	1.50	0.9332	2.00	0.9772
0.01	0.5040	0.51	0.6950	1.01	0.8438	1.51	0.9345	2.02	0.9783
0.02	0.5080	0.52	0.6985	1.02	0.8461	1.52	0.9357	2.04	0.9793
0.03	0.5120	0.53	0.7019	1.03	0.8485	1.53	0.9370	2.06	0.9803
0.04	0.5160	0.54	0.7054	1.04	0.8508	1.54	0.9382	2.08	0.9812
0.05	0.5199	0.55	0.7088	1.05	0.8531	1.55	0.9394	2.10	0.9821
0.06	0.5239	0.56	0.7123	1.06	0.8554	1.56	0.9406	2.12	0.9830
0.07	0.5279	0.57	0.7157	1.07	0.8577	1.57	0.9418	2.14	0.9838
0.08	0.5319	0.58	0.7190	1.08	0.8599	1.58	0.9429	2.16	0.9846
0.09	0.5359	0.59	0.7224	1.09	0.8621	1.59	0.9441	2.18	0.9854
0.10	0.5398	0.60	0.7257	1.10	0.8643	1.60	0.9452	2.20	0.9861
0.11	0.5438	0.61	0.7291	1.11	0.8665	1.61	0.9463	2.22	0.9868
0.12	0.5478	0.62	0.7324	1.12	0.8686	1.62	0.9474	2.24	0.9875
0.13	0.5517	0.63	0.7357	1.13	0.8708	1.63	0.9484	2.26	0.9881
0.14	0.5557	0.64	0.7389	1.14	0.8729	1.64	0.9495	2.28	0.9887
0.15	0.5596	0.65	0.7422	1.15	0.8749	1.65	0.9505	2.30	0.9893
0.16	0.5636	0.66	0.7454	1.16	0.8770	1.66	0.9515	2.32	0.9898
0.17	0.5675	0.67	0.7486	1.17	0.8790	1.67	0.9525	2.34	0.9904
0.18	0.5714	0.68	0.7517	1.18	0.8810	1.68	0.9535	2.36	0.9909
0.19	0.5753	0.69	0.7549	1.19	0.8830	1.69	0.9545	2.38	0.9913
0.20	0.5793	0.70	0.7580	1.20	0.8849	1.70	0.9554	2.40	0.9918
0.21	0.5832	0.71	0.7611	1.21	0.8869	1.71	0.9564	2.42	0.9922
0.22	0.5871	0.72	0.7642	1.22	0.8888	1.72	0.9573	2.44	0.9927
0.23	0.5910	0.73	0.7673	1.23	0.8907	1.73	0.9582	2.46	0.9931
0.24	0.5948	0.74	0.7704	1.24	0.8925	1.74	0.9591	2.48	0.9934
0.25	0.5987	0.75	0.7734	1.25	0.8944	1.75	0.9599	2.50	0.9938
0.26	0.6026	0.76	0.7764	1.26	0.8962	1.76	0.9608	2.55	0.9946
0.27	0.6064	0.77	0.7794	1.27	0.8980	1.77	0.9616	2.60	0.9953
0.28	0.6103	0.78	0.7823	1.28	0.8997	1.78	0.9625	2.65	0.9960
0.29	0.6141	0.79	0.7852	1.29	0.9015	1.79	0.9633	2.70	0.9965
0.30	0.6179	0.80	0.7881	1.30	0.9032	1.80	0.9641	2.75	0.9970
0.31	0.6217	0.81	0.7910	1.31	0.9049	1.81	0.9649	2.80	0.9974
0.32	0.6255	0.82	0.7939	1.32	0.9066	1.82	0.9656	2.85	0.9978
0.33	0.6293	0.83	0.7967	1.33	0.9082	1.83	0.9664	2.90	0.9981
0.34	0.6331	0.84	0.7995	1.34	0.9099	1.84	0.9671	2.95	0.9984
0.35	0.6368	0.85	0.8023	1.35	0.9115	1.85	0.9678	3.00	0.9987
0.36	0.6406	0.86	0.8051	1.36	0.9131	1.86	0.9686	3.05	0.9989
0.37	0.6443	0.87	0.8078	1.37	0.9147	1.87	0.9693	3.10	0.9990
0.38	0.6480	0.88	0.8106	1.38	0.9162	1.88	0.9699	3.15	0.9992
0.39	0.6517	0.89	0.8133	1.39	0.9177	1.89	0.9706	3.20	0.9993
0.40	0.6554	0.90	0.8159	1.40	0.9192	1.90	0.9713	3.25	0.9994
0.41	0.6591	0.91	0.8186	1.41	0.9207	1.91	0.9719	3.30	0.9995
0.42	0.6628	0.92	0.8212	1.42	0.9222	1.92	0.9726	3.35	0.9996
0.43	0.6664	0.93	0.8238	1.43	0.9236	1.93	0.9732	3.40	0.9997
0.44	0.6700	0.94	0.8264	1.44	0.9251	1.94	0.9738	3.50	0.9998
0.45	0.6736	0.95	0.8289	1.45	0.9265	1.95	0.9744	3.60	0.9998
0.46	0.6772	0.96	0.8315	1.46	0.9279	1.96	0.9750	3.70	0.9999
0.47	0.6808	0.97	0.8340	1.47	0.9292	1.97	0.9756	3.80	0.9999
0.48	0.6844	0.98	0.8365	1.48	0.9306	1.98	0.9761	3.90	1.0000
0.49	0.6879	0.99	0.8389	1.49	0.9319	1.99	0.9767	4.00	1.0000
0.50	0.6915	1.00	0.8413	1.50	0.9332	2.00	0.9772		

Appendix 3: Binomial cumulative distribution function

The tabulated value is $P(X \leq x)$, where X has a binomial distribution with index n and parameter p.

$p =$	0.05	0.10	0.15	0.20	0.25	0.30	0.35	0.40	0.45	0.50
$n = 5, x = 0$	0.7738	0.5905	0.4437	0.3277	0.2373	0.1681	0.1160	0.0778	0.0503	0.0312
1	0.9774	0.9185	0.8352	0.7373	0.6328	0.5282	0.4284	0.3370	0.2562	0.1875
2	0.9988	0.9914	0.9734	0.9421	0.8965	0.8369	0.7648	0.6826	0.5931	0.5000
3	1.0000	0.9995	0.9978	0.9933	0.9844	0.9692	0.9460	0.9130	0.8688	0.8125
4	1.0000	1.0000	0.9999	0.9997	0.9990	0.9976	0.9947	0.9898	0.9815	0.9688
$n = 10, x = 0$	0.5987	0.3487	0.1969	0.1074	0.0563	0.0282	0.0135	0.0060	0.0025	0.0010
1	0.9139	0.7361	0.5443	0.3758	0.2440	0.1493	0.0860	0.0464	0.0233	0.0107
2	0.9885	0.9298	0.8202	0.6778	0.5256	0.3828	0.2616	0.1673	0.0996	0.0547
3	0.9990	0.9872	0.9500	0.8791	0.7759	0.6496	0.5138	0.3823	0.2660	0.1719
4	0.9999	0.9984	0.9901	0.9672	0.9219	0.8497	0.7515	0.6331	0.5044	0.3770
5	1.0000	0.9999	0.9986	0.9936	0.9803	0.9527	0.9051	0.8338	0.7384	0.6230
6	1.0000	1.0000	0.9999	0.9991	0.9965	0.9894	0.9740	0.9452	0.8980	0.8281
7	1.0000	1.0000	1.0000	0.9999	0.9996	0.9984	0.9952	0.9877	0.9726	0.9453
8	1.0000	1.0000	1.0000	1.0000	1.0000	0.9999	0.9995	0.9983	0.9955	0.9893
9	1.0000	1.0000	1.0000	1.0000	1.0000	1.0000	1.0000	0.9999	0.9997	0.9990
$n = 20, x = 0$	0.3585	0.1216	0.0388	0.0115	0.0032	0.0008	0.0002	0.0000	0.0000	0.0000
1	0.7358	0.3917	0.1756	0.0692	0.0243	0.0076	0.0021	0.0005	0.0001	0.0000
2	0.9245	0.6769	0.4049	0.2061	0.0913	0.0355	0.0121	0.0036	0.0009	0.0002
3	0.9841	0.8670	0.6477	0.4114	0.2252	0.1071	0.0444	0.0160	0.0049	0.0013
4	0.9974	0.9568	0.8298	0.6296	0.4148	0.2375	0.1182	0.0510	0.0189	0.0059
5	0.9997	0.9887	0.9327	0.8042	0.6172	0.4164	0.2454	0.1256	0.0553	0.0207
6	1.0000	0.9976	0.9781	0.9133	0.7858	0.6080	0.4166	0.2500	0.1299	0.0577
7	1.0000	0.9996	0.9941	0.9679	0.8982	0.7723	0.6010	0.4159	0.2520	0.1316
8	1.0000	0.9999	0.9987	0.9900	0.9591	0.8867	0.7624	0.5956	0.4143	0.2517
9	1.0000	1.0000	0.9998	0.9974	0.9861	0.9520	0.8782	0.7553	0.5914	0.4119
10	1.0000	1.0000	1.0000	0.9994	0.9961	0.9829	0.9468	0.8725	0.7507	0.5881
11	1.0000	1.0000	1.0000	0.9999	0.9991	0.9949	0.9804	0.9435	0.8692	0.7483
12	1.0000	1.0000	1.0000	1.0000	0.9998	0.9987	0.9940	0.9790	0.9420	0.8684
13	1.0000	1.0000	1.0000	1.0000	1.0000	0.9997	0.9985	0.9935	0.9786	0.9423
14	1.0000	1.0000	1.0000	1.0000	1.0000	1.0000	0.9997	0.9984	0.9936	0.9793
15	1.0000	1.0000	1.0000	1.0000	1.0000	1.0000	1.0000	0.9997	0.9985	0.9941
16	1.0000	1.0000	1.0000	1.0000	1.0000	1.0000	1.0000	1.0000	0.9997	0.9987
17	1.0000	1.0000	1.0000	1.0000	1.0000	1.0000	1.0000	1.0000	1.0000	0.9998
18	1.0000	1.0000	1.0000	1.0000	1.0000	1.0000	1.0000	1.0000	1.0000	1.0000

Appendix 4: Poisson cumulative distribution function

The tabulated value is $P(X \leq x)$, where X has a Poisson distribution with parameter μ.

$\mu =$	0.5	1.0	1.5	2.0	2.5	3.0	3.5	4.0	4.5	5.0
$x = 0$	0.6065	0.3679	0.2231	0.1353	0.0821	0.0498	0.0302	0.0183	0.0111	0.0067
1	0.9098	0.7358	0.5578	0.4060	0.2873	0.1991	0.1359	0.0916	0.0611	0.0404
2	0.9856	0.9197	0.8088	0.6767	0.5438	0.4232	0.3208	0.2381	0.1736	0.1247
3	0.9982	0.9810	0.9344	0.8571	0.7576	0.6472	0.5366	0.4335	0.3423	0.2650
4	0.9998	0.9963	0.9814	0.9473	0.8912	0.8153	0.7254	0.6288	0.5321	0.4405
5	1.0000	0.9994	0.9955	0.9834	0.9580	0.9161	0.8576	0.7851	0.7029	0.6160
6	1.0000	0.9999	0.9991	0.9955	0.9858	0.9665	0.9347	0.8893	0.8311	0.7622
7	1.0000	1.0000	0.9998	0.9989	0.9958	0.9881	0.9733	0.9489	0.9134	0.8666
8	1.0000	1.0000	1.0000	0.9998	0.9989	0.9962	0.9901	0.9786	0.9597	0.9319
9	1.0000	1.0000	1.0000	1.0000	0.9997	0.9989	0.9967	0.9919	0.9829	0.9682
10	1.0000	1.0000	1.0000	1.0000	0.9999	0.9997	0.9990	0.9972	0.9933	0.9863
11	1.0000	1.0000	1.0000	1.0000	1.0000	0.9999	0.9997	0.9991	0.9976	0.9945
12	1.0000	1.0000	1.0000	1.0000	1.0000	1.0000	0.9999	0.9997	0.9992	0.9980
13	1.0000	1.0000	1.0000	1.0000	1.0000	1.0000	1.0000	0.9999	0.9997	0.9993
14	1.0000	1.0000	1.0000	1.0000	1.0000	1.0000	1.0000	1.0000	0.9999	0.9998
15	1.0000	1.0000	1.0000	1.0000	1.0000	1.0000	1.0000	1.0000	1.0000	0.9999
16	1.0000	1.0000	1.0000	1.0000	1.0000	1.0000	1.0000	1.0000	1.0000	1.0000
17	1.0000	1.0000	1.0000	1.0000	1.0000	1.0000	1.0000	1.0000	1.0000	1.0000
18	1.0000	1.0000	1.0000	1.0000	1.0000	1.0000	1.0000	1.0000	1.0000	1.0000
19	1.0000	1.0000	1.0000	1.0000	1.0000	1.0000	1.0000	1.0000	1.0000	1.0000
$\mu =$	5.5	6.0	6.5	7.0	7.5	8.0	8.5	9.0	9.5	10.0
$x = 0$	0.0041	0.0025	0.0015	0.0009	0.0006	0.0003	0.0002	0.0001	0.0001	0.0000
1	0.0266	0.0174	0.0113	0.0073	0.0047	0.0030	0.0019	0.0012	0.0008	0.0005
2	0.0884	0.0620	0.0430	0.0296	0.0203	0.0138	0.0093	0.0062	0.0042	0.0028
3	0.2017	0.1512	0.1118	0.0818	0.0591	0.0424	0.0301	0.0212	0.0149	0.0103
4	0.3575	0.2851	0.2237	0.1730	0.1321	0.0996	0.0744	0.0550	0.0403	0.0293
5	0.5289	0.4457	0.3690	0.3007	0.2414	0.1912	0.1496	0.1157	0.0885	0.0671
6	0.6860	0.6063	0.5265	0.4497	0.3782	0.3134	0.2562	0.2068	0.1649	0.1301
7	0.8095	0.7440	0.6728	0.5987	0.5246	0.4530	0.3856	0.3239	0.2687	0.2202
8	0.8944	0.8472	0.7916	0.7291	0.6620	0.5925	0.5231	0.4557	0.3918	0.3328
9	0.9462	0.9161	0.8774	0.8305	0.7764	0.7166	0.6530	0.5874	0.5218	0.4579
10	0.9747	0.9574	0.9332	0.9015	0.8622	0.8159	0.7634	0.7060	0.6453	0.5830
11	0.9890	0.9799	0.9661	0.9467	0.9208	0.8881	0.8487	0.8030	0.7520	0.6968
12	0.9955	0.9912	0.9840	0.9730	0.9573	0.9362	0.9091	0.8758	0.8364	0.7916
13	0.9983	0.9964	0.9929	0.9872	0.9784	0.9658	0.9486	0.9261	0.8981	0.8645
14	0.9994	0.9986	0.9970	0.9943	0.9897	0.9827	0.9726	0.9585	0.9400	0.9165
15	0.9998	0.9995	0.9988	0.9976	0.9954	0.9918	0.9862	0.9780	0.9665	0.9513
16	0.9999	0.9998	0.9996	0.9990	0.9980	0.9963	0.9934	0.9889	0.9823	0.9730
17	1.0000	0.9999	0.9998	0.9996	0.9992	0.9984	0.9970	0.9947	0.9911	0.9857
18	1.0000	1.0000	0.9999	0.9999	0.9997	0.9993	0.9987	0.9976	0.9957	0.9928
19	1.0000	1.0000	1.0000	1.0000	0.9999	0.9997	0.9995	0.9989	0.9980	0.9965
20	1.0000	1.0000	1.0000	1.0000	1.0000	0.9999	0.9998	0.9996	0.9991	0.9984
21	1.0000	1.0000	1.0000	1.0000	1.0000	1.0000	0.9999	0.9998	0.9996	0.9993
22	1.0000	1.0000	1.0000	1.0000	1.0000	1.0000	1.0000	0.9999	0.9999	0.9997